Composition and Communication Workbook

CIS 110 and CIS 111

Sarah Kercsmar, PhD | Renee Kaufmann, MA

CENGAGE
Learning·

Australia • Brazil • Japan • Korea • Mexico • Singapore • Spain • United Kingdom • United States

**Composition and Communication Workbook:
CIS 110 and CIS 111**
Sarah Kercsmar, PhD | Renee Kaufmann, MA

Executive Editors:
Maureen Staudt
Michael Stranz

Senior Project Development Manager:
Linda deStefano

Marketing Specialist:
Courtney Sheldon

Senior Production/Manufacturing Manager:
Donna M. Brown

Production Editorial Manager:
Kim Fry

Sr. Rights Acquisition Account Manager:
Todd Osborne

For product information and technology assistance, contact us at
Cengage Learning Customer & Sales Support, 1-800-354-9706

For permission to use material from this text or product,
submit all requests online at **cengage.com/permissions**
Further permissions questions can be emailed to
permissionrequest@cengage.com

Compilation © 2012 Cengage Learning

ISBN-13: 978-1-285-11939-7

ISBN-10: 1-285-11939-8

Cengage Learning
5191 Natorp Boulevard
Mason, Ohio 45040
USA

Cengage Learning is a leading provider of customized learning solutions with office locations around the globe, including Singapore, the United Kingdom, Australia, Mexico, Brazil, and Japan. Locate your local office at:
international.cengage.com/region.

Cengage Learning products are represented in Canada by Nelson Education, Ltd.

For your lifelong learning solutions, visit **custom.cengage.com.**

Visit our corporate website at **cengage.com.**

Printed in the United States of America

Composition and Communication Workbook

Sarah Kercsmar, PhD, Eds. and Renee Kaufmann, MA, Eds.

TABLE OF CONTENTS
Composition and Communication I and II

[Composition and Communication II:]

INTRODUCTION

What is the C&C Sequence?

WHAT IS THE COMPOSITION AND COMMUNICATION (C&C) SEQUENCE?

While in many universities first-year composition and oral communication are taught as separate courses, the University of Kentucky General Education curriculum recognizes that speaking, writing, and using visuals effectively are interrelated skills. The Composition and Communication I and II courses are designed to engage students in composing and communicating ideas using speech, writing, and visuals in an active learning environment. Both courses participate in the broad learning objectives of developing critical thinking and information literacy skills within an academic context that emphasizes the problems students will confront as educated citizens of the twenty-first century. Students will practice composing, critiquing, and revising ideas for audiences and in developing public speaking and interpersonal communication skills. Cultivating life-long habits of writing and speaking for personal expression and community participation is an important goal of this curriculum. The proficiencies demonstrated in these courses will then be reinforced throughout the students' major course of study. This workbook was first designed to be used with the courses at UK, but has found wider appeal as other universities adopt similar courses.

ICEBREAKERS AND INTRODUCTORY MATERIALS

Autograph Party

Unique and Shared

What's Your Color?

Blackboard Scavenger Hunt

AUTOGRAPH PARTY

Goal: This activity is designed to help you get to know your classmates.

Rationale: One of the primary reasons people experience communication anxiety is because they have a "fear of the unknown." Part of this fear stems from the fact that their audience is made up of strangers. One way to reduce this fear and, consequently, reduce the anxiety that stems from it, is to engage in activities that acquaint speakers with their listeners before they actually present a formal speech.

Directions: Try to find a classmate who fits each description below. Have the classmate sign this sheet next to the appropriate description. You must find *a different* person for each description. Each person may sign only one line.

FIND SOMEONE WHO

. . . is an only child. ——————————————

. . . skipped breakfast today. ——————————————

. . . drives a foreign car. ——————————————

. . . was born west of the Mississippi River. ——————————————

. . . isn't getting enough sleep. ——————————————

. . . plays a musical instrument. ——————————————

. . . was born in July. ——————————————

. . . is a parent. ——————————————

. . . is left-handed. ——————————————

. . . engages in aerobic activity. ——————————————

. . . has an unusual hobby. ——————————————

. . . is married. ——————————————

. . . knows someone whom you know. ——————————————

. . . has schedule problems. ——————————————

. . . writes poetry. ——————————————

. . . has traveled overseas. ——————————————

. . . is in love. ——————————————

. . . speaks a language besides English. ——————————————

. . . has the same major as you. ——————————————

. . . has eaten liver and onions. ——————————————

Taken from "Com 181: Public Speaking Workbook" Deanna Sellnow

UNIQUE AND SHARED

Goal: This activity is designed to help you get to know your classmates.

Rationale: One of the primary reasons people experience communication anxiety is because they have a "fear of the unknown." Part of this fear stems from the fact that their audience is made up of strangers. One way to reduce this fear and, consequently, reduce the anxiety that stems from it, is to engage in activities that acquaint speakers with their listeners before they actually present a formal speech.

Directions: Form groups of five people. The first half of the activity is the "shared" part. There needs to be a notetaker for each group to create a list of many common traits or qualities that members of the group have in common. Avoid writing things that are immediately obvious (e.g., don't write down something like "everyone has hair" or "we are all wearing clothes"). The goal is for everyone to dig deeper than the superficial. Your group has five to six minutes to construct the list and then one person will act as a spokesperson from each subgroup to read their list to the entire class.

Rationale: Revealing "shared" information first will allow students to see commonalties with their fellow classmates and will aid in further disclosing "unique" information. (Keeping in mind the goal for building relationships within the classroom.)

Shared:

UNIQUE AND SHARED – PART II

Directions: The second half is the "unique" part. Keep the same groups. Below record unique traits and qualities; that is, items that only apply to one person in the group. Each group will need to find at least two unique qualities and strengths per person. Again, strive for qualities and strengths beyond the superficial and past the obvious things anyone can readily see. Your group will have five to six minutes. When time is up, share the unique qualities in one of the following ways: (1) each person can share one of their unique qualities themselves; (2) have each person read the qualities of the person to their right; or (3) have a spokesperson read a quality one at a time, and have the others guess who it was.

Unique:

WHAT'S YOUR COLOR?

Goal: This activity is designed to help you get to know your classmates.

Rationale: One of the primary reasons people experience communication anxiety is because they have a "fear of the unknown." Part of this fear stems from the fact that their audience is made up of strangers. One way to reduce this fear and, consequently, reduce the anxiety that stems from it, is to engage in activities that acquaint speakers with their listeners before they actually present a formal speech.

Directions: Pick an M and M out of the bag and remember what color you have (if you eat it). We will go around the room and introduce ourselves…using the M and Ms as a conversation starter.

Red: What is your favorite outdoor activity?

Orange: Name your favorite subject in school as a child – and tell us why.

Green: Who is the most popular music artist today and why?

Blue: If you were going to a desert island and could only take one thing with you, what would that be and why?

Created by Sarah Kercsmar, University of Kentucky

BLACKBOARD SCAVENGER HUNT

Name: _____ Section: _____

Goal: To familiarize students with Blackboard early in the semester.

Rationale: Educational technology, like Blackboard, may seem confusing and unclear if you haven't used it before. This activity provides you an opportunity to jump in and explore quickly.

Directions: In order to complete this scavenger hunt, you will need to log-in to your Blackboard (Bb) shell for this course. Please bring any challenges you have in completing this worksheet to class next time and we will discuss then.

1. The first thing I see when I enter this course on Bb is:

2. The syllabus for this class can be found under the _____ tab.

3. My instructor's office hours are:

4. To find my grades for the course, I would go to:

5. To submit my first essay/assignment, I would go to:

6. What is one question you have about using Bb that you'd like to talk about during the next class?

Created by Sarah Kercsmar, University of Kentucky

Composition and Communication I: Discovering Self & Learning from the Community

INTERPERSONAL COMMUNICATION

Self-Concept & Perception

Conflict Management & Resolution

Nonverbal & Verbal Communication

Interpersonal Relationships

SELF-IDENTITY: FROM TV TO REAL LIFE

Goal: This worksheet will challenge you to identify the roles that the tv characters play...and then brainstorm about your own self-identity.

Rationale: When we're asked to describe ourselves, we often say things like "student" or "daughter," and while these words are very accurate descriptors, we could learn the same information by looking at a student ID card or a birth certificate.

Directions: Choose one of the tv shows below and watch an episode and then answer the questions about the character's self-identity.

1. **Mike and Molly (CBS):** Observe Molly and answer the questions about her self-identity.

2. **White Collar (USA):** Observe Neil and answer the questions about his self-identity.

3. **The Middle (ABC):** Observe Axl and answer the questions about his self-identity.

4. **Glee (FOX):** Observe Mercedes and answer the questions about her self-identity.

REFLECTION QUESTIONS

1. Write down everything that comes to mind about your character in 2 minutes.

2. Now, look at your list and circle the items that you could learn about your character either by just looking at them or talking to them for 5 minutes or less. Do you have any words that aren't circled?

3. Take 5 more minutes and think beyond the obvious. How would you describe the character's self-identity in more depth? If you were going to do a speech of self-introduction about your character, what would be really interesting and novel for the audience?

4. Compare your two lists. Write a paragraph about the differences between the two lists – and your thought process in moving from very obvious to less obvious.

YOUR TURN

1. Describe your self-identity in 2 minutes. Don't think too hard – just write. (Bullet points are fine.)

2. Now, look at your list and circle the items that people could earn about you either by just looking at you or talking to you for 5 minutes or less. Do you have any words that aren't circled?

3. Take 5 more minutes and think beyond the obvious. How would you describe your own self-identity in more depth? If you were going to do a speech of self-introduction about yourself, what would be really interesting and novel for the audience?

4. Compare your two lists. Write a paragraph about the differences between the two lists – and your thought process in moving from very obvious to less obvious.

Created by Sarah Kercsmar, University of Kentucky

I'D PREFER TO BE.....

Goal: To evaluate what traits you consider most desirable for your self-concept and why.

Rationale: Self-concept is often tied up with our perception of others. This exercise challenges you to consider how your own self-perceptions are formed from the perceptions of others.

Directions: Rank each of the traits listed in each set from 1-3. One should be your most preferred and 3 is your least preferred. Be prepared to discuss your rankings.

1. _____ intelligent
   _____ wealthy
   _____ physically attractive

2. _____ a movie star
   _____ a senator
   _____ a successful businessperson

3. _____ on an average date
   _____ reading an average book
   _____ watching an average television show

4. _____ loved
   _____ feared
   _____ respected

5. _____ applying for a job by letter
   _____ applying by face-to-face interview
   _____ applying by telephone interview

6. _____ successful in my social life
   _____ successful in my family life
   _____ successful in business life

7. _____ angry
   _____ guilty
   _____ fearful

8. _____ a leader
   _____ a follower
   _____ a loner

Modified from an assignment created by Nikki Blau, Ohio University – Lancaster

"YOUR 3 WORDS" ASSIGNMENT

Goal: To challenge you to define your self-concept succinctly in both spoken and visual formats.

Rationale: This course integrates oral, written, and visual communication throughout. In this assignment, the emphasis is on oral and visual communication.

Directions: As part of exploring your self-concept and roles in life, choose any three words that express who you are, reflect your mood, define yourself, etc. The three words can be individual words or three words that make up a short phrase.

The words need to be creatively displayed, and then you need to video yourself (or take a photo if you can't use video) displaying the three words.

Examples of this type of display from ABC's "Good Morning America's" segment are available at http://abcnews.go.com/GMA/Your3Words/.

A special segment with multiple examples is online at http://abcnews.go.com/US/words-live-event-good-morning-america/story?id=14469378

Remember that you must be in the video/photo, but you can include others in it as well. Get creative!

We'll look at them in class and discuss why you chose those three words.

Contributed by Allyson DeVito, University of Kentucky

FIRST IMPRESSIONS: PERCEPTIONS OF OTHERS

Goal: To introduce the idea of perception of others.

Rationale: As we move from perception of self to perception of others, this exercise challenges you to think about how quickly we form first impressions of others.

Directions: Your group was given a picture of a person in an envelope. Take the picture out of the envelope and answer the questions individually as I read them aloud. After all the questions, you will compare answers with the other people in your group. Finally, you'll describe the person to the rest of the class to see if they can guess what the person in your picture does/looks like.

1. What is the person's job?

2. How much money do they make?

3. Do they have a family? Kids? How many?

4. What kind of car do they drive?

5. What would you find this person doing on a typical Saturday afternoon?

6. What kind of books does this person like to read?

7. What is their favorite movie?

8. What is their favorite type of music?

9. What is their favorite food?

10. Where do they live?

CONFLICT CASE STUDY

Goal: To apply conflict management strategies to a real-life situation.

Rationale: Sometimes, topics talked about in the classroom can feel short of real-life applicability. This exercise provides an intersection between the classroom and the "real world."

Directions: Below is a true-life conflict situation. Read the story and then discuss the five different ways this conflict might be potentially managed (or mismanaged) by those parties involved based on the 5 conflict strategies identified in your text: **Avoidance, Accommodating, Competition, Compromise, Collaborating.** Come up with scenarios of how might they manage or mismanage their issues according to each of these 5 types.

SCENERIO: Laura and Julie are best friends and roommates. They live in a small, two bedroom, two bathroom condominium in an apartment complex with no private yard. They have similar personalities, both are laid-back, fun-loving, and reserved, so living together has been relatively easy and conflict free. However, recently, Julie's boyfriend got her a medium-sized dog for her birthday. Laura has grown up with dogs, and is genuinely excited about the prospect of having a dog around the apartment. The dog, while not a puppy, is young and excitable (hyper). Although it is potty-trained, it still has some "accidents." Both Laura and Julie work long hours at their jobs where they are gone extended periods of time and often have to work strange hours. Never having had a dog of her own to train before, Julie decides to leave the dog out to roam free in the apartment while she is gone to work or other events. This has resulted in some incidents with bathroom accidents and chewed up furniture. Julie always tries to clean up and fix what her dog has damaged after these incidents, but some things, such as a chewed up couch cushion, cannot be fixed, and sometimes her roommate Laura gets home to the mess before she does.

Julie realizes there is a problem, and tries to figure out various solutions, such as putting baby gates up in the kitchen doorway to confine the dog while she is gone, but to no avail. The dog jumps over the gates and gets out. Up until this point Laura has been okay with the dog and the incidents, but she works long, late hours and when she comes home to a messy house and a hyper dog, it is a real imposition on her to take care of these problems when it isn't even her dog. She holds in her feelings until resentment starts to build, and then finally when the dog gets to be too much, she writes Julie a note with a list of grievances and a demand that Julie find the dog a new home. Although Julie understands Laura's feelings, Julie is hurt and upset that Laura did not approach the situation differently and earlier, and feels betrayed by her best friend. Also, Julie genuinely loves the dog and doesn't want to give him up. Her boyfriend who gave her the dog has his own apartment, but he has roommates and a rigorous schedule too.

In your group, outline the possibilities of how this conflict might play out according to the 5 conflict management strategies below. Be specific with your scenarios!

1. **Avoidance**

2. **Accommodating**

3. **Competition**

4. **Compromise**

5. **Collaboration**

What would be the best option given the situation, the relationship, and the two people involved? Why?

Created by Kelly Cowden, University of Kentucky

USING LANGUAGE ETHICALLY: ETHICAL CRITIQUE PRACTICE

Goal: To practice ethical critiquing.

Rationale: When evaluating peers' essays or speeches, it is easy to say "looks great" and move on. More specific feedback, both positive and negative, is much more helpful to peers.

Directions: A good ethical critique has four parts to it:

1. Constructive Criticism: Positive and Negative Critiques

2. Specific

3. Accompanied by a Rationale (explain)

4. Phrased in terms of the Listener's Perception ("I")

Revise each critique below to make it a more ethical critique. Remember, a good critique does all 4 things.

EXAMPLE:

Original critique: Good eye contact.

Revised critique: I thought you used good eye contact during your introduction. I felt like you were talking to me and that made me more engaged in your speech throughout. I thought when you started using a lot of statistics in the middle of the speech, you weren't using eye contact as much to help me understand what you were talking about. Maybe you could consider writing less on your notecards next time so you can connect with us more.

Original critique: Speech was hard to hear.
Revised critique:

Original critique: Essay thesis doesn't make sense.
Revised critique:

Original critique: PowerPoint slide was lousy.
Revised critique:

Original critique: Essay was great.
Revised critique:

Created by Sarah Kercsmar, University of Kentucky

POLITICAL POSTURING: NONVERBAL COMMUNICATION IN POLITICS

Goal: To evaluate nonverbals in a video clip.

Rationale: Actions often speak louder than words. By evaluating someone else's nonverbals, you can also consider what your own nonverbal say in your communication interactions.

Directions: Watch a speech of a local or national politician giving a speech. Thinking about what you've learned about nonverbal communication, describe what the politician's nonverbals are saying about his or her feeling toward the topic and/or the audience. When a politician is trying to win an election, what they "say" with their body is often more important than what they are saying with their words.

Kinesics:

Haptics:

Paralanguage:

Proxemics:

Chronemics:

Appearance:

Created by Sarah Kercsmar, University of Kentucky

TOO MUCH SELF-DISCLOSURE?

Goal: To evaluate the level and type of disclosure found in social media.

Rationale: Individuals often disclose things in cyberspace that they never would in face-to-face inter-actions. This activity allows you to consider inappropriate disclosures in cyberspace.

Directions: Have you ever noticed that people tell complete strangers their life stories online? One of the keys to interpersonal relationships is appropriate self-disclosure. You are going on a scavenger hunt for inappropriate self-disclosures online. PLEASE NOTE: To protect the innocent, don't use any names when you share the disclosures.

Disclosure 1:

Social media site (i.e. Facebook, Twitter, Pinterest, etc.):

Relationship between the person who is disclosing and the people reading the disclosure:

Inappropriate Self-Disclosure:

What makes it inappropriate:

Disclosure 2:

Social media site (i.e. Facebook, Twitter, Pinterest, etc.):

Relationship between the person who is disclosing and the people reading the disclosure:

Inappropriate Self-Disclosure:

What makes it inappropriate:

Disclosure 3:

Social media site (i.e. Facebook, Twitter, Pinterest, etc.):

Relationship between the person who is disclosing and the people reading the disclosure:

Inappropriate Self-Disclosure:

What makes it inappropriate:

Free-Write: What do the inappropriate self-disclosures you've shared have in common? When would the level of disclosure found here be appropriate (if ever)? How does self-disclosure make you feel – when are you comfortable with it and when are you uncomfortable with it?

Created by Sarah Kercsmar, University of Kentucky

WRITTEN COMMUNICATION

Writing Process: Brainstorming

Writing Process: Drafting

Writing Process: Editing & Revising

Writing Process: Peer Review

BRAINSTORMING FOR PROJECT 1 ESSAY: SELF-CONCEPT & IDENTITY

Goal: To help you brainstorm potential main points for your project 1 essay.

Rationale: Sometimes you need help organizing your ideas or figuring out where to start for an essay. Writing the first few words can be the most difficult task. This exercise provides questions to help you organize your thoughts for the first essay.

Directions: Your instructor may have you choose some, or all, of these questions to use as a brainstorming tool for your essay.

- Why did you choose the photo you picked for this assignment?

- What does it reveal about who you were or are or hope to be?

- What are some of the adjectives you would to describe who you were when you were younger?

- What are the traits you would use to describe yourself today?

- What are the characteristics that you would want someone to use to describe you in ten years? Why?

- How are who you were, who you are, and who you want to be similar or different from one another?

- How does your picture provide content for your essay?

- What are some ways you can crop your image? In which order will you show the cropped images?

- How does the way your crop your photo help impact what you might say about yourself?

- How would other people describe you?

- What about who you are has remained constant throughout the years?

- What about you do you think has changed (dramatically or slightly) over time?

- How will the traits you possess now help you in the future?

- How did this moment in time shape your self-concept then? Does it continue to shape your self-concept?

- What has happened since the photograph was taken that has solidified your self-concept or threatened it?

- What do you want your future or ideal self-concept to look like? Why?

- How does the picture relate to your identity and face?

- How does this photo tie you to a larger community? Or represent you as a part of a group or culture?

Contributed by Brandi Frisby, University of Kentucky

FROM CLUSTERING/MAPPING TO EXPLODING PARAGRAPHS

Goal: To provide two brainstorming/drafting tools – clustering/mapping and exploding paragraphs.

Rationale: Many times when we get ready to write, we open a new document only to watch the cursor blink unceasingly against the blank screen. It almost seems to be mocking us. Write something. Write something! Writer's Block takes over. Our minds are blank to any idea that can help us develop our paper.

Directions: In this exercise, let's take a different approach. Ignore the cursor on the screen for a minute and instead, get out a piece of paper and a pencil/pen.

1. In the middle of the page, write down three topics that represent you or are of interest to you. I've chosen Family, Pets, and Travel. Draw a circle around these three topics and then draw three lines out from this circle (see illustration on next page).

2. Think about each of these three topics. On the lines drawn out from the circle, write down as many sub-topics as you can think of for each of the original topics. For example, I wrote down Mom and Sister beside the Family tab.

3. After you have written the sub-topics, circle each one. Then rank them 1 through 3.

4. Now we're going to focus on the topic that got your top rating. Draw five lines out from circle you labeled #1. For example, I ranked 'Africa' first.

5. Think about at least five topics that are associated with your new #1 topic. Write these topics on the lines you just drew. For example, I wrote 'Food', 'Artwork', 'Weather', 'Language', and 'Clothing'.

6. After you have these topics listed around the topic you ranked #1, turn your paper over. List your #1 ranked topic and draw a line under it. Then number your paper 1 to 5. Now you can list the five topics you brainstormed about on the previous page.

7. Finally, we're ready to go back to your new document and face that blinking cursor. Take each of the five topics you listed on the back of your paper and write a paragraph about each one. When you are finished writing these paragraphs, go back and add some more to each one. Think about details and visual images. Take the reader into each of these topics.

8. Now it's time to 'Explode These Paragraphs'. Take each paragraph and write as much as you can about each topic. When you think you can't write anymore, write another sentence. These paragraphs can be a page or so long, it's OK. You'll work more on organization of these ideas in the next stage of writing your paper. Right now, the most important idea is to get that content on the page.

9. See, doesn't that feel good? Now save your document, stick your tongue out at the blinking cursor, and get ready to put these paragraphs to good use in your paper.

Contributed by Carla Bevins, University of Kentucky

Example for Clustering/Mapping to Exploding Paragraphs

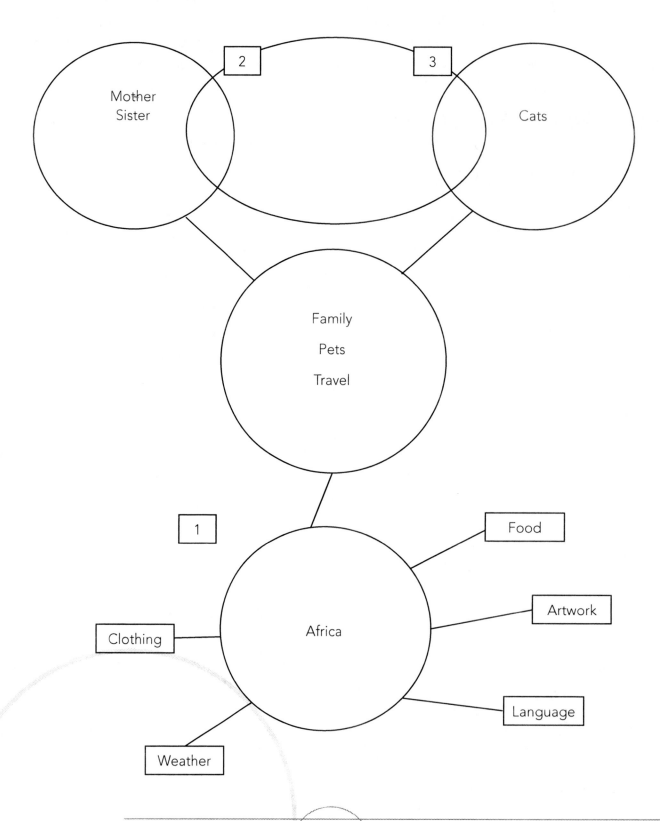

DRAFTING THESIS STATEMENTS

Goal: To provide practice creating good thesis statements.

Rationale: Good thesis statements are the central idea of an essay. They cover what is in the essay – nothing more, nothing less. After reading your thesis statement, your audience should understand the "flavor" of the essay. Moving from a general topic to a clear, concise thesis statement can sometimes be a challenge.

Directions: Following the example provided, move each subject below through the steps to end with a good thesis statement.

EXAMPLE:

Subject: Summer job possibilities

Statement of fact: Summer jobs can be hard to find for college students.

Announcement: In this essay, I will describe why summer jobs can be hard to find for college students.

Thesis statement: Although summer jobs may be few in your hometown, planning ahead by making connections can help college students secure a well-paying, summer job.

Subject: Things to do in your hometown

Statement of fact:

Announcement:

Thesis statement:

Subject: Your essay 1 topic:

Statement of fact:

Announcement:

Thesis statement:

Created by Sarah Kercsmar, University of Kentucky

THESIS STATEMENTS

Goal: To provide practice identifying, correcting, and creating thesis statements.

Rationale: This 3-step thesis statement process (identifying, correcting, and creating) allows you to see how other writers have used thesis statements and then to create some of your own.

Directions: Idenfity the thesis statement in each of the introductions presented below by underlining the sentence(s) that state the main idea. After locating the thesis statement, circle the 2-3 main points the author previews that will be discussed in the body of the essay.

Essay Introduction 1:

> Identities, according to the *Merriam Webster Dictionary*, are the distinguishing character or personality of an individual. Your identity as a person is what your most prominent trait it is. With what you do you *identify*? I have multiple identities as a student, a coach, a daughter and granddaughter, but the one I believe I identify with most is being a sibling and a daughter. These two identities shaped me in the past, the present and the future.

Essay Introduction 2:

> Finding who you are can be one of the most challenging things you ever do. For me, it took more time and patience than I wanted to give to the search. Throughout my life I had always been the loud girl who was always really outgoing and friendly, that never changed, but I was completely unsure of who I really was deep down. Now, in my freshman year of college, I can finally say I'm completely, undoubtedly sure I have found myself. There is little that I am one hundred percent sure of, but there are three things I know for sure. I was lost and unable to find myself. I am now a college student moving on with self-assurance with her best friend by her side. Lastly, I hope to be the best mother and teacher that I can possibly be.

Essay Introduction 3:

My Life as an Academic

Some people can leave work at work; academics are not those people. When your job and your identity are tied together, work is hard to leave at the office. Looking back at what has brought me to a faculty office at the University of Kentucky, I see how my identity as an academic has been shaped by my life at the same time that this identity molded the trajectory of my life (figure 1). My identity as a scholar has been an important part of who I was growing up, who I am today, and who I hope to be in the future.

Bad Thesis Statement:

In this essay I will explain how my job has influenced my self-concept and identity.

Corrected Thesis Statement:

Bad Thesis Statement:

I spent many years playing sports with my dad in our backyard. Eventually I became a member of a great Fraternity at school and many lessons I learned with my dad proved to be important.

Corrected Thesis Statement:

Bad Thesis Statement:

Being a member of a band is extremely important to me. I play the bass guitar and I really enjoy playing Metallica and AC/DC with my friends. I've learned a lot from them.

Corrected Thesis Statement:

Now, write 2-3 thesis statements for your own essay. Try writing 2-3 versions of the same thesis statement or write thesis statements for 2-3 different topics. *(Use separate paper as needed)*

1. _____
   _____
   _____

2. _____
   _____
   _____

3. _____
   _____
   _____

Created by Anna Rankin, University of Kentucky

WRITING PROCESS: EDITING AND REVISING

Goal: To provide practice in the editing step of the writing process.

Rationale: While editing isn't all about "mechanics," good mechanics are an important part of a well-written essay.

Directions: Please edit to improve grammar, structure, and style.

Advertising is everywhere in American society today. It is almost with us at every moment throughout the day. From the moment we wake up and the radio blaring loudly to when we are getting ready to sleepily turn off the television late at night. It has such a strong foothold in American society that we rarely even bother that we are being targeted by all of these different companies from everywhere. They place ads in target areas to reach their audience in order to sell their product. The more and more exposure that they get to people, the more and more known their products are and that's the main goal companies strive for. Advertisers also have ways of making people think differently by invoking certain emotions within the consumers by influencing the consumer's thoughts and ethics, they can trust up an ad many different ways to match the scenario that they want. It is up to the consumer to decide to whether or not they bought the message that the advertiser is trying to convey.

Created by Brandi Frisby, University of Kentucky

WRITING PROCESS: WRITING EFFECTIVE SENTENCES

Goal: To provide practice in the editing/revising step of the writing process.

Rationale: Effective sentences make effective paragraphs and effective paragraphs make effective essays. This exercise provides you with practice with the "building block" of a good essay–a good sentence.

Directions: Revise these sentences to be clear and concise.

- Although France bit off more than they could chew in Vietnam, America's intervention was too little, too late.
- Democracy is really good for practically everyone.
- All of our hopes and dreams were fulfilled when Adrian became first and foremost in the public eye after saving the entire planet.
- The reason for the failure of the economic system of the island was the inability of Gilligan in finding adequate resources without incurring expenses at the hands of the headhunters on the other side of the island.
- Today, society is witnessing the steady progression of women towards equality with their increasing presence in the working world and in government and their gradual move outside the home.
- Due to circumstances beyond our control, a number of in-process documents are currently inaccessible.

Created by Brandi Frisby, University of Kentucky

PEER REVIEW GUIDELINES

While there are many ways to review the work of others, it is important to keep the purpose of your review in mind – to help provide helpful and ethical feedback. Below are some guidelines for ethical feedback when reviewing a peer's written work.

Ethical Feedback:

➠ Make positive and negative statements

➠ Use "I" language

➠ Be specific

➠ Provide rationale

While reading the paper:

➠ Ask questions that will help with the clarity of the paper:

- Why does…
- Where…
- What do you mean…
- How…

➠ Don't focus strictly on conventions (punctuation, spelling, grammar). If the errors are so bad they interfere with the paper's message, make some corrections and include a comment about it in the concluding feedback.

You will want to include some type of summative statement that explains what you thought of the paper. It would be helpful and beneficial for the writer to include:

➠ What you liked about the overall paper. Explain what you thought the writer did well. Be specific!

➠ What you thought the writer could improve upon or include to help with the paper's purpose or message. Be specific!

➠ Any other suggestions, comments, or concerns.

Modified from "Com 181: Public Speaking Workbook" Deanna Sellnow

ORAL COMMUNICATION

Speech Anxiety

Listening and Responding

Audience Analysis

Public Speaking Overview

Outlining

Rehearsal Day

Speech Day

COPING WITH ANXIETY:
TECHNIQUES FOR CONTROLLING YOUR SPEECH ANXIETY

1. **Be prepared to speak.** One of the biggest causes of speech anxiety is lack of preparation. If you think you can research a topic, organize your materials, type your outline, prepare your notes, practice your speech without relying on your notes, and incorporate a visual aid or object, *on the night before you are scheduled to speak*, *you* most certainly *will* have speech anxiety.

2. **Focus on your message.** If you concentrate on getting your message across to the listener rather than thinking about what your audience is thinking of you, you should experience less speech anxiety.

3. **Nobody "bats" 1000!** Understanding that you will make some mistakes while speaking should help you to keep the speaking situation in perspective. The important thing about the speech experience is that the audience *wants you* to succeed. As a speaker, let the little mistakes go by—there is very little you can do once they occur—and keep the main ideas coming through clearly. When your speech is over, your audience will most likely not even remember what you thought were "major league" errors.

4. **Never apologize for your nervousness.** Although some beginning speakers believe alerting an audience to their nervousness will enhance their effectiveness, it is not true. Letting listeners know about our nervousness usually causes them to focus on our symptoms of nervousness rather than on our message.

5. **Keep the speech in perspective.** After all, the speech is simply "a speech." When it is over you should still be breathing. Your life will go on as it did before you spoke. Try not to put additional pressure on yourself by overemphasizing the importance of the speaking opportunity.

6. **Try mental and physical exercises to help reduce your speech anxiety.** There are many exercises you might try to reduce your speech anxiety that include mental and physical exercises. Try thinking of your favorite spot—a quiet place where you have peace and solitude for a few minutes just before you get up to speak. Although certain strenuous physical exercises help relieve the stress of having to speak, they are not always possible moments before you must speak in a class or public meeting. As such, try isometric exercises which might involve making a tight grip with your hands, pressing your fingers or palms together, or pushing your heels together prior to speaking. Taking a deep breath before rising to speak also releases pent up nervousness.

7. **Monitor your speech anxiety while you speak.** Even though you might feel as if the entire class were observing your knees shaking or hearing your voice quiver, usually the speech anxiety you experience is not as obvious as you might think. You might try to gesture or even move from one point to another in front of your audience. Pushing down on your big toes—without locking your knees—while speaking can also help to drive your nervousness right out.

8. **As a safeguard, build a visual aid and/or physical activity into your speech.** Showing the object or visual aid will help you concentrate more on your speech and less on your nervousness.

Taken from "Com 181: Public Speaking Workbook" Deanna Sellnow

HOW WELL DO YOU LISTEN? A REFLECTIVE EXERCISE

Goal: To encourage reflection on listening skills in various situations.

Rationale: How well we listen often varies by situation or person that we are interacting with. Listening, in general, can be difficult, but the level of difficulty can vary depending on the situation.

Directions: Answer the questions below in preparation for the class discussion on listening.

1. In one of your classes, add an extra column to your class notes. Put a star beside places in the lecture where you find your mind starting to wander. After class, look through your notes and see if there are particular times or topics where you were distracted the most. Do you know what was distracting you?

2. Pick a phone call with a person you talk to a lot (maybe your mom or your best friend). Pay attention during the conversation to whether you stay focused on the conversation…or do you find yourself planning what you are going to say next while you are "listening?" After you are done with the call, reflect on the difference between hearing and listening in this conversation.

3. Choose a face-to-face conversation you've had recently. Was it easier or harder to use active listening face-to-face than on the phone? Why do you think that was?

4. Do you consider yourself a good listener? Why or why not?

Created by Sarah Kercsmar, University of Kentucky

AUDIENCE ANALYSIS

Goal: To help you consider how your audience affects how you will approach your speech topic.

Rationale: Everything from demographics to predisposition to a topic can affect how you approach a speech topic and should be considered in planning your main points and overall game plan for a speech.

Directions: Complete the questionnaire below with the audience for your next speech in mind.

Steps of Audience Analysis

Step 1
Determine – Who is your audience?

Step 2
Write down the specifics.

Step 3
Research the audience using resources such as the library, websites, statistical indexes, and interviews.

Step 4
Use the information you gather to complete the following checklist.
You may want to add or omit items from the checklist depending on the specifics of your audience and speech.

Audience Analysis Checklist (from Verderber 2000)

1. The audience education level is:

____ high school ____ college ____ post college

2. The age is from ____ to ____. The average age is about ____.

3. The audience is approximately ____% male and ____% female.

4. My estimate of the income level of the audience is:

____ below average ____ average ____ above average

5. The audience is basically ____ the same race ____ a mixture of races

6. The audience is basically:

____ the same religion ____ a mixture of religions

7. The audience is basically:

____ the same nationality ____ a mixture of nationalities

8. The audience is basically from:

____ the same state ____ the same city

____ the same neighborhood ____ different areas

Step 5

Use your analysis to predict the audience's response to your topic.

1. Audience interest in this topic is likely to be:

____ high ____ moderate ____ low

2. Audience understanding of the topic will be:

____ great ____ moderate ____ little

3. Audience attitude about me as a speaker is likely to be:

____ positive ____ neutral ____ negative

4. Audience attitude toward my topic will be:

____ positive ____ neutral ____ negative

Adapted from Heaton, Dan. Public Address lecture. Capital University, Columbus, OH. Fall 2003. UNCG University Speaking Center, (336)256-1346, speakingcenter.uncg.edu

AUDIENCE ANALYSIS: WHO YOU ARE COMMUNICATING WITH MATTERS!

Goal: To consider how the same topic can be communicated to different audiences.

Rationale: Whether you are writing or speaking, considering your audience carefully matters.

Directions: You have been assigned the topic of safety issues in dorms and/or apartments. Consider each audience below as you complete the worksheet.

<u>Resident Assistants</u>

Two most interesting points:

Convincing evidence:

Possible visual aid for speech:

<u>College Freshmen</u>

Two most interesting points:

Convincing evidence:

Possible visual aid for speech:

<u>Parents</u>

Two most interesting points:

Convincing evidence:

Possible visual aid for speech:

<u>Your C & C Instructor</u>

Two most interesting points:

Convincing evidence:

Possible visual aid for speech:

Differences between writing about the topic and giving a speech on the topic:

The Lexington-Herald Leader

Two most interesting points:

Convincing evidence:

MAJOR COMPONENTS OF PUBLIC SPEAKING

Effective public speaking is centered on three major areas: content, structure, and delivery. If you can master skills in each of these areas, you can become a competent communicator in public speaking situations.

Content To have good content, you need to consider the purpose of your speech and make sure your message adheres to that purpose. In other words, if you are presenting an informative speech, be sure you are not trying to get listeners to change their behavior. Likewise, if your purpose is an actuation persuasive speech, be sure to provide an action step telling listeners what they should do to eliminate the problem or improve the situation. Your analysis should also offer reasoning that is rooted in ethos (ethical appeals), pathos (emotional appeals), and logos (logical appeals). You can also achieve this by making sure your speech rounds the entire cycle of learning, that is, addresses feeling, thinking, watching, and doing.

Make sure your supporting material is varied, accurate, evenly distributed, and properly credited. Finally, offer breadth, depth, and listener relevance links throughout the speech; that is, consider these elements *for each main point*. Listener relevance links are statements that remind listeners how your information relates to some aspect of their life. As a goal, answer this question for each main point: How will listeners benefit from hearing this?

Structure Effective structure means offering your ideas in an orderly framework so listeners can follow your train of thought. Macrostructural elements have to do with the elements of the outline itself. Microstructural elements have to do with language choices you make to articulate your ideas. Language should be accurate, clear, inclusive, and vivid. You should avoid language that marginalizes or stereotypes members of your audience. You should also only use technical jargon when you define it in simple language. And you should avoid using slang terms or "verbal garbage" (uhms, uhs, like, and ya know) to fill pauses in the presentation. The following is a "Generic Public Speech Outline," which explains the macrostructural components of an effective public speech.

Delivery Effective delivery means you employ effective use of voice, effective use of body, and effective presentational aids.

Use of Voice

1. Effective use of voice means being intelligible. In other words, do you use an appropriate rate, volume, and pitch that helps listeners understand what you are saying?

2. In addition to intelligibility, you need to sound conversational. To clarify, do you sound like you are talking with your listeners rather than presenting in front of them or reading to them?

3. You also need to sound fluent. You need crisp articulation, enunciation, and pronunciation. Your phrases should sound smoothly connected rather than choppy and disconnected.

4. Effective use of voice also means using vocal variety in ways that make you sound committed to the topic and occasion. If your speech is something you are excited about, you ought to sound excited. If it is a serious speech, you ought to sound serious. If it is humorous, you ought to sound like you are having fun with it.

Use of Body

1. Effective use of body means being poised. Do you appear confident, comfortable and "in control?"

2. Effective use of body also has to do with attire. You should dress up a bit more than your listeners dress in order to appear credible and committed.

3. You also need to avoid engaging in distracting nonverbal cues such as fidgeting with your notes, playing with your hair, or shifting and swaying. These actions need to be avoided because they can distract listeners from the message and "leak" nervousness.

4. Effective use of body also means using effective eye contact. Doing so means using direct eye contact, looking listeners in the eye as opposed to over their heads. It also means spanning the entire room (even the corners and edges), turning your entire head as you do so. Finally, it means relying on your notes only 5–10 percent of the time. These notes are a speaking outline comprised of key words, phrases, and delivery cues. Your reliance on them should be minimal.

5. Effective use of body also means using facial expressions, gestures, and motivated movement only in ways that *reinforce* the verbal message. They should reinforce an emotional attitude or clarify structure. If they do not, they are distracting nonverbal cues and should be eliminated.

Presentational Aids

Construction

1. Visual presentational aids need to be large enough for everyone to see easily (even in the back of the room).

2. Visual presentational aids must consist of a symbol system beyond just words alone (e.g., photograph, diagram, map, chart).

3. Visual presentational aids must enhance credibility (neat, colorful, professional-looking).

4. Audio and audiovisual presentational aids much be loud enough to be heard in the back of the room, but not so loud as to hurt those in the front of the room.

5. Audio and audiovisual presentational aids must not take too much time to play during the speech (no more than about 5% of your total speaking time).

Integration

1. Conceal visual presentational aids until you want to share them.

2. Reveal only what you want your audience to see.

3. Conceal visual presentational aids when you have finished that topic.

4. Be sure to refer (gesture to/touch) to your presentational aid when discussing its content.

5. Be sure to credit the source of your presentational aid as an oral footnote during the speech.

GENERIC FORMAL OUTLINE MAP

INTRODUCTION:

Here you should write out the introduction. Label the required parts of the introduction as you compose it:

I. **Attention Catcher** (This statement serves two functions: it catches listeners' attention and tunes them into your topic. You may use a rhetorical question, a direct question, a humorous anecdote, a famous quotation, a hypothetical example, an actual example, a startling statistic, and so on.)

II. **Listener Relevance** (Once you have your listeners' attention, you need to reveal why they should listen to this particular speech. How does this material affect them? Why should they care?)

III. **Speaker Credibility** (In this step, you need to let listeners know why they should listen to you in particular. How/Why do you know more about this topic than they do? You may have personal experience with the topic; you may have researched extensively; you may have written articles about the topic. The point is, let your listeners know at the outset that you know a good deal about the topic.)

IV. **Thesis Statement** (This one-sentence summary of your speech is formed by, first, combining the general purpose to inform, to persuade, to entertain, to introduce, and the specific purpose about what? Be sure to state your thesis quite clearly. If listeners miss this part, they will have difficulty following the rest of the speech.)

V. **Preview** (In this statement, alert your listeners to the main points of your speech. As with the thesis statement, be very clear so listeners can easily follow the organizational pattern of the speech.)

BODY

[**CONNECTIVE/TRANSITION:** Make sure your audience knows you are moving from the introduction into the first main point.]

I. One complete sentence that expresses the main point of this section of the speech.

Listener Relevance Link: Develop your connection to the audience in one to two sentences.

    A. **Subpoint** (These supporting points help listeners understand your perspective. They learn why you stated your main point in the way you did. Consider breadth, depth, and listener relevance as you support each main point.)

    1. Sub-subpoint

      a. Sub-sub-subpoint

      b. Sub-sub-subpoint

    2. Sub-subpoint

  B. Subpoint

    1. Sub-subpoint

    2. Sub-subpoint

  C. Subpoint

[**CONNECTIVE/TRANSITION:** Create a connective to help the audience move from the first main point to the second.]

  II. Here is another complete sentence expressing the main point of this section of the speech.

Listener Relevance Link: Develop your connection to the audience in one to two sentences.

  A. Subpoint

    1. Sub-subpoint

    2. Sub-subpoint

  B. Subpoint

    1. Sub-subpoint

    2. Sub-subpoint

      a. Sub-sub-subpoint

      b. Sub-sub-subpoint

      c. Sub-sub-subpoint

        i. Sub-sub-sub-subpoint

        ii. Sub-sub-sub-subpoint

    3. Sub-subpoint

[**CONNECTIVE/TRANSITION:** Make sure your audience knows you are moving to the conclusion.]

CONCLUSION

Here you write out the conclusion. Label the required parts as you compose them:

    I. **Thesis Restatement** (You may simply use the Thesis statement from the introduction, changing it to past tense.)*

    II. **Main Point Summary:** (Remind listeners of the two to four main points about which you elaborated during the speech.) *

    III. **Clincher** (The clincher serves several functions: provides closure, often ties back to the attention catcher, heightens speech to aid in retention, helps listeners remember....."Thank you" is NOT a clincher.)

REFERENCES

Here you list complete citations, in APA format, for the research materials you have used in your speech. **Include your citations in the body of the outline.**

[**NOTE:** *The ordering of the Thesis Restatement and Main Point Summary can be reversed.]

Taken from "Com 181: Public Speaking Workbook" Deanna Sellnow

SELF-REFLECTION

NAME: _____

Goal: To evaluate you own performance during your rehearsal speech.

Rationale: As a form of cognitive restructuring, this exercise can help reduce public speaking anxiety.

Directions: Watch your practice speech and add to it as you watch yourself on the recording.

1. Overall, I would give myself a grade of _____ on my practice speech because….

2. One thing that surprised me when I watched the recording was…..

3. To improve as a public speaker on my speech, I am going to try to…..

**Next make any necessary changes to your speaking and/or formal outlines. And remember to practice, practice, practice!
Taken from "Com 181: Public Speaking Workbook" Deanna Sellnow

ASKING QUESTIONS: YOUR RESPONSIBILITY AS AN AUDIENCE MEMBER

An audience member in a scholarly setting is not simply expected to sit back and listen. Their job is to actively — provocatively — work toward a dialogue in which audience and presenters together explore topics, issues, and problems.

WHAT IS A "GOOD" QUESTION?

A "good" question opens discussion rather than close it off. And good questions come out of engaged, active listening. As you listen and take notes, ask yourself two questions:

1. **What have you learned?** How has this presenter or session challenged what you thought you knew about a topic?

2. **What's behind or beyond this presentation?** What larger histories, broader theories, or wider range of experience does the session gesture toward?

STRATEGIES FOR CONSTRUCTING A QUESTION

From these questions you ask yourself, you can then construct questions to pose to the presenter(s) or your peers in the audience. How?

- **Listen for questions that presenters themselves pose but do not pursue.** Scholarship poses questions, explicitly or implicitly. Which ones interest you?

- **Listen for keywords.** Scholarship often works by asking us to think through new definitions for familiar concepts. Are you finding these new definitions useful? Are there dark areas they leave unlit? Are there other ways YOU might redefine these keywords?

- **Listen for the intellectual problem or larger public issue the presentation addresses.** Do you accept their challenge to the scholarly consensus or the conventional wisdom? Do you want to hear more about the intellectual stakes or the practical implications of their challenge?

- **Draw connections among presentations.** One purpose of public presentation is to create opportunities for a dynamic cross-pollination of ideas. Point to ways that the presentations complement one another, and ask presenters to comment. Are you seeing unexpected convergences, or equally unexpected divergences? Does the discussion you've heard in other conference sessions have anything to contribute to this one?

Draw upon your own experience and knowledge. Scholarship is not produced in a vacuum. What experiences, theories, or ideas have you been working with, as a scholar or as a human being, that might be of interest to the presenter(s) or your peers in the audience?

Taken from George Washington University: http://www.gwu.edu/~capstone/symposium/asking_questions.htm

INTERCULTURAL COMMUNICATION

Community Based Research

BRAINSTORMING FOR PROJECT 2: COMMUNITIES

Goal: To help you brainstorm potential communities to observe for your project 2 essay.

Rationale: Exploring communities that are different from our own in some area of intercultural communication (i.e. race, class, gender, sexual orientation, religion, etc.) helps us challenge our own perceptions and think about why we see the world as we do.

Directions: First, brainstorm communities you are currently a part of and not a part of, compare with your classmates as directed by your instructor, and then answer the questions below.

COMMUNITIES I AM A PART OF	COMMUNITIES I AM NOT A PART OF
1.	1.
2.	2.
3.	3.
4.	4.
5.	5.

1. Which communities are you most interested in learning about and why (Top 3)?

2. Who are classmates with whom you had a common interest to complete Project #2?

Created by Brandi Frisby, University of Kentucky

EXAMPLES OF COMMUNITIES FOR PROJECT 2

When it's time to pick a community for Project 2, you might find yourself scratching your head saying "what should I study?" The possibilities are endless. Here are three examples of communities that would be appropriate choices.

PLEASE NOTE: *These communities are just EXAMPLES and if you want to use one of the communities below, you MUST talk with your instructor ahead of time – and make a good case for doing so since they were provided as examples.*

If you are interested in local food production, consider....

The Lexington Farmers' Market (http://www.lexingtonfarmersmarket.com/)
The LFM is held outside on Saturday, Sunday, Tuesday, and Thursday (locations vary) from April – October. There is a smaller indoor market during the winter time. This community is made up of farmers/local product vendors and customers. You could study the community from the perspective of a farmer/local product vendor by spending time with them over the course of a few markets or from the perspective of the customers. You could also compare the communities at the markets held on different days of the week. Does the location make the experience different?

If you are interested in learning about a new faith community, consider...

The University of Kentucky Newman Center (http://newmancenter.home.insightbb.com/)
The UK Newman Center is the spiritual home for Catholic students, faculty, and staff on campus. In addition to attending weekly Mass to learn about the community, you could also meet with the staff, attend a student organization meeting or two, and examine the physical space of the Newman Center. What stereotypes do you have about the Catholic faith? Did they change after your time at the Newman Center?

If you are interested in sports or kids, consider....

The Toyota Bluegrass Miracle League (http://www.bluegrassmiracleleague.org/)
The TBML is a baseball league for children ages 5-19 with a special need, mental or physical. The league runs in the spring and the fall. This community is made up of players, parents, and volunteers who assist with the games. You could study the community from the perspective of one specific group or the TBML as a whole. How do the kids interact with one another? How do the kids interact with the adult volunteers? Do the parents have a community of their own and what does it look like?

PRACTICE: WANDERING ANALYSIS

Goal: To provide practice in doing field observations and interviewing.

Rationale: Sometimes when we observe a piece of art, a situation, or a community, we only see things at the surface level. This will provide an opportunity to look below the surface – and then compare what you see with a partner.

Directions: In pairs, go find a piece of art on campus. Choose something that catches your attention, but is still part of the ordinary landscape in fresco. You are to complete this worksheet individually, without talking to your partner. After you have completed the worksheet, you will take turns interviewing each other about what you saw.

Take a picture of the object using your phone camera.

1. Stand 10 feet away from that object and list every minute detail – nothing is too trivial to note. Take at least 5 minutes looking at this distance.

2. Now, stand immediately in front of your object. Use your other senses – touch it, smell it, etc. (as appropriate). Take care to have an understanding of all of the parts that make up the whole object. Take at least 5 more minutes with your object and continue to make notes on your observation.

Contributed by Raj Gaur, University of Kentucky

ASSUMPTIONS ABOUT MY COMMUNITY

Name _____ Community _____

Goal: To examine your beliefs about your community before you start studying it.

Rationale: We have preconceived notions about most things in life – and examining those ideas before we start spending time in a community allows us to really think about what we learn in the process.

Directions: Complete the questions as directed by your instructor.

I currently believe these things about my community:

Why do I believe these things?

I believe that others stereotype my community in this way:

Where do these stereotypes come from? Are they positive or negative?

Created by Brandi Frisby, University of Kentucky

RESEARCH STRATEGIES AND TOOLS

Secondary Research

Primary Research

Using and Integrating Sources

Ignite

LIBRARY RESEARCH

Goal: To explore what information is already available using online resources about your community.

Rationale: Before going into a community, it is important to first do some secondary research on a topic to see what is already written about your community.

Directions: Complete the worksheet below using the online resources that can be found through the library's webpage below.

Names_____

1. What did you learn from researching your topic in the Gale Virtual Reference Library?

2. What subjects are related to your topic in Academic Search Premier?

3. Name a scholarly article that you might use. What makes you think it might be relevant to your project?

4. Are you able to access this article? If so, how? If not, what other scholarly article can you use?

5. What newspaper article could you use for this topic? Name it here:

6. What subjects in the online catalog are helpful?

7. Name one book, its location, and its call number, that you could use in your project.

Created by Marcia Rapchack, Duquesne University

EVALUATING ONLINE RESOURCES PAIR WORK

Goal: To explore what information is already available using online resources about your community.

Rationale: Before going into a community, it is important to first do some secondary research on a topic to see what is already written about your community.

Directions: Complete the worksheet below using the online resources described below.

Names _____

Go to Google.com. Search for your community and answer the following questions.

1. How many hits did you receive?

2. How could you limit the number of hits?

Go to Google Advanced Search (http://www.google.com/advanced_search) and narrow your search. Answer the following questions:

3. What were your search terms?

4. How many hits did you receive?

Click on a website that looks promising (not Wikipedia, though Wikipedia can be a good start. If you look at Wikipedia, use one of the external links it provides at the bottom of the page). Answer the following information about the source:

5. Who is the author? Are his or her credentials known? If so, what are those credentials and how might they be relevant to the topic? If you can't find an author, why might this be a problem?

6. When was the source published? How might this date (or lack of date) matter if you use this resource in your project?

7. Who is the intended audience? How can you tell?

8. What is the purpose of this piece?

9. Does this resource substantially or only superficially cover your topic? Why might this coverage matter if you used this resource in your project?

10. Does this source cite other resources? What does this use or nonuse of other resources show you about your resource?

11. What must you consider before using this resource in a project (i.e. biases, conflicting information, currency issues, etc.)? What would you need to tell your audience about this resource if you used it in your project?

12. List as many ways as possible that you could use this resource in an essay or speech on your topic.

Go to Google Scholar (http://scholar.google.com/) and search for your community.

13. How many hits did you receive?

14. Do any sources look useful? If so, list them.

Click on Advanced Google Scholar, and narrow your search to be more relevant to your assignment.

15. How many hits did you receive?

16. What did you search and in what fields?

17. List two useful sources you see.

Created by Marcia Rapchack, Duquesne University

EVALUATING SOURCES

Goal: To evaluate the utility and credibility of a variety of sources on a particular topic.

Rationale: All sources are not created equal. Some are too old, some are not credible, and some just aren't a great fit for your topic. This exercise asks you to consider all those issues.

Directions: You are writing a paper about "college freshman at a public university." **Skim** the four sources you have been provided and *briefly* evaluate them using the criteria below. Then, identify information you might use in an essay on the topic (if applicable).

	WEBSITE (UKY.EDU)	WEBSITE (EHOW.COM)	JOURNAL ARTICLE	NEWSPAPER
Authority How credible are the author(s), publication, sponsors, etc? Are they "experts" on the topic?				
Stance What is the purpose of the piece? Are their clear biases?				
Currency When was the piece published? How does this influence the credibility of the source?				
Relevance Is the information appropriate for the topic?				
Accuracy Are the conclusions made based on a sufficient amount of data?				
Multiplicity Does the source provide multiple perspectives? Does the author cite other sources?				

Adapted from a worksheet created by Anna Rankin, University of Kentucky

YES OR NO....OR TELL ME MORE

Goal: To practice creating good interview questions.

Rationale: When preparing for an interview with a person in the community you're observing, you want to create questions that will get the "most bang for your buck," while not being intrusive or too time-consuming.

Directions: Consider whether the questions below would help you gain the insight you need into your community. Each example also asks you to construct a follow-up question that would help you gain more insight.

1. How long have you been part of this community?

        Circle one: Good Question   Bad Question   Depends

Why?

Follow-Up Question:

2. Is there any conflict among community members?

        Circle one: Good Question   Bad Question   Depends

Why?

Follow-Up Question:

3. Describe a typical meeting with your group.

      Circle one: Good Question   Bad Question   Depends

Why?

Follow-Up Question:

4. Do you like participating within your community?

      Circle one: Good Question   Bad Question   Depends

Why?

Follow-Up Question:

5. For someone who is new to your community, what would you say are the most important things to learn about your group?

      Circle one: Good Question   Bad Question   Depends

Why?

Follow-Up Question:

Created by Sarah Kercsmar, University of Kentucky

FIELD NOTES TEMPLATE

Goal: To provide a template for taking field notes during your community observations.

Rationale: Taking field notes involves two parts – observation and assigning meaning. This exercise will provide you practice in doing both parts.

Directions: You should set any pre-conceived notions you may have aside during the observation stage and just report on what you observe using all 5 senses. During the assigning meaning phase, think about the "why" behind "what" you observed.

OBSERVATION (THE "WHAT")	MEANING (THE "WHY")
See	
Hear	
Smell	
Touch	
Taste	
Other	

Created by Sarah Kercsmar, University of Kentucky

APA CITATION PRACTICE

Goal: To familiarize you with proper APA citation formats.

Rationale: APA citation style is often new to students in this course. Hands-on practice allows you to work through citations as a group.

Directions: Complete the worksheet sections as described below.

1. As a group, find the section in your handbook that discusses APA citations and references. Find the sample citations for books and journal articles.

2. Using APA format, each person should practice referencing by making a citation for the *Composition and Communication* textbook. The following are questions you should answer as you make the citation.

   a. *Who* are the authors? How should their names be written?

   b. *When* was the book published?

   c. *Where* was the book published?

   d. How should the title appear in the citation?

3. Exchange your citation with a partner and correct each other's citations.

4. Compare your citations as a group and come to a conclusion about what the correct format is for the citation. Share with the class.

5. Using the following information, put these citations in proper APA format. Finalize your citations as a group before we share as a class.

Journal Article, One Author
Author: G. Ku
Year: 2008
Article title: "Learning to De-Escalate: The Effects of Regret in Escalation of Commitment."
Journal Title: Organizational Behavior and Human Decision Processes
Vol. 105 Issue 2
pg. 221-232.

Journal Article, Multiple Authors
Authors: Mark Van Vugt, Robert Hogan, and Robert B. Kaiser
Year: 2008
Article title: Leadership, followership, and evolution: Some lessons from the past.
Journal title: *American Psychologist*
Volume 63
Issue 3
p. 182-196

6. Now, as a group, look up in-text citations in APA format. Answer the following questions as a group before we discuss as a class.

   a. How should in-text citations appear? What do they look like?

   b. Why are in-text citations used in a paper? What is their purpose?

   c. What is the difference between in-text citations for *paraphrasing* versus *direct quotations*?

IGNITE: ENLIGHTEN US BUT MAKE IT QUICK

WHAT IS IGNITE?

Ignite is a fast-paced geek event started by Brady Forrest, Technology Evangelist for O'Reilly Media, and Bre Pettis of Makerbot.com, formerly of MAKE Magazine. Speakers are given 20 slides, each shown for 15 seconds, giving each speaker 5 minutes of fame.

From: Ignite, 2011, **http://igniteshow.com/howto**

Ignite

- If you attend Ignite you will see rapid-fire presentations from all segments of the community designed to inspire and connect.
- No animation allowed in slides
- No pitches allowed

Purpose highlights the efforts and passions of the local community as a whole; trying to inspire, inform, and presenting/creating new ways of thinking and doing things

From: IgniteWiki, 2011, **http://wiki.igniteshow.com/wiki/index.php/Main_Page**

COMPOSITION AND COMMUNICATION I SAMPLE ESSAYS & OUTLINES

Project 1 Essays

Project 1 Outlines

Project 2 Essays

Project 2 Outlines

Project 1 Essay: I am a Beatnik

Cassandra Hummert

Professor Holly Roberts

CIS 110

7 October 2011

"Here's to the crazy ones. The misfits. The rebels. The troublemakers. The round pegs in the square holes - the ones who see things differently. They're not fond of rules and they have no respect for the status quo. You can praise them, disagree with them, quote them, disbelieve them, glorify or vilify them. About the only thing that you can't do is ignore them. Because they change things."

I Am

This quote by Jack Kerouac defines a generation of unconventional young people in the 1950's. I am an unconventional of the 21ˢᵗ century. Born in a small town and raised on a farm, I found my identity through a mix of hard work and a small private school education. My family, my friends, my hobbies and my future are what some may define as unconventional. I like to say that I'm a beatnik. Not a redneck and not a hippie, but as Merriman Webster states, "a young, free spirited non-conformist". Throughout my life I've struggled with having to conform while still trying to find an identity for myself. At this point in my life, however, I am proud of who I am, and feel that I've found that mix of free spirit and conformity. There are many aspects of my childhood and education that have had an important impact on my life as a beatnik. In this paper I will use the above picture to tell a little bit about my growing up such as my hobbies, my home, and my high school career and how they have made me the person I am today.

I grew up on a 55-acre horse farm in Northeast, Ohio, where the work is never ending and the winters are unbearably cold. I was always surrounded by nature, though, and developed a real appreciation for what we as people get from the land and how to give back to it. As you can see in the picture to the right, I used the example of the cattails in the lake to show this. Growing up with horses meant a lot of early mornings trudging out in the rain and the mud. I hated it. I wanted to be like kids who lived in some suburbia

development with their mom and dad and 1-½ brothers or sisters. I wanted to be able to sleep in until ten minutes before the bus picked me up for school. I wanted to wear something nice to school and straighten my hair. Instead, I showed up to grade school dressed in dirty jeans and smelling like a horse. As I got older though, and watched my classmates go to soccer or baseball or other typical 7th grader activities, I found my sanctuary in riding horses. I was blessed to have horses on our property and be able to ride and be with them whenever I wanted. I would go out by myself for hours, trailblazing through the woods, sitting quiet and listening to the stillness in the air. We had one pony, whose name was Thor, and he became my favorite. Every day I would take extra special care of him, and pretty soon declared him "mine". Thor was a trooper, and put up with all of my crazy endeavors. He traveled to horse shows, continuously got bathed, and jumped every homemade split rail obstacle that I put in front of him. I learned a lot from Thor, such as having to put in effort to achieve something. This lesson can be applied in so many areas of life, and I was lucky to learn that lesson at a pretty young age, but it is something that no one can perfect, as I found out in high school. Having these opportunities, however, played a major part in making me grateful for what I had. I began to focus less on what everyone else was doing, and more on what I wanted to do, which was escape every day after school. I was beginning to define myself and use my surroundings and my home to shape who I am- someone who does not conform to the "norm".

Although I grew up on a farm, I went to a conservative private high school in nearby Hudson, Ohio. I was thrown into an environment that I had previously done a good job of avoiding. Now I was surrounded by a bunch of Republican rich kids with nice cars and inflated egos. I had gotten so wrapped up in my stereotypes of the "other side" that now that I was

integrated with them, I couldn't seem to shake those preconceived notions, and instead completely withdrew. My first
two years of high school were horrible. I didn't have many
friends, I didn't get good grades, and I struggled to keep my
life together. I just wasn't involving myself with this new place
at which I had to spend a lot of time. I was forgetting that
lesson that I had learned growing up, about getting out what
one puts in. It would take a drastic move to make a change in
my last few years of high school. So finally, during the beginning of my junior year, I made the decision that I was going to
change. I wanted to become involved, and started by meeting
one new person a day. As I started to interact and get involved
with my classmates as well as the spirit of my school, I realized

that many of my former notions were wrong. I had things in common with them, and when my
senior year started I had really good friends and was having a blast. I went to my senior prom, as
shown in the picture above, and had the time of my life. I was the farm girl who, even though I
woke up every morning to clean horse stalls, could clean up and wear a dress and have fun and
party. It was an identity that I was beginning to accept. I was starting to find a balance in my life
with school and horses. I had changed tremendously, but the values that I had developed growing up on the farm were still with me, and were only made stronger as I applied them to the real
world, and I finished high school a well-rounded, intelligent young adult who could make smart
decisions.

The last thing that I am going to talk about that has
shaped me into the fun-loving unconventional beatnik
that I am is my love of the outdoors and hobbies and
the connection with my family. I am generally outgoing
about new things, and my dad has played an important
role in pushing me to do things that I might otherwise
have not done. In the picture to the right I am holding a
fishing pole. My dad taught me how to fish, and some of
my fondest memories are of him and I sitting on the edge

of the dock, waiting for one of our bobbers to dip below the surface of the water. I remember when I was younger my dad and I fishing, him with his fishing hat, and me with my little blue plastic Mickey Mouse fishing pole. I caught what I thought was a huge fish, and was so excited that I jumped up and lost my balance and fell in the water. From then on it was the half-pound bluegill that had pulled me in. I take pride in other unconventional things that I've done. I've traveled the world, whether it was buying horses in Germany, or spending the summer in Fiji helping out children in the highlands. I have shown horses around the country, and most recently traveled to New Jersey for the Pan-American games selection trials. I also spent this past summer driving racecars in southern Ohio, and was not only the youngest driver, but also the only girl. Despite the unorthodox nature of all these endeavors, my family has supported me through whatever crazy dream or summer plan I have decided to pursue. I love that

I can say these things about myself at the young age of eighteen, and I have a never-ending list of things I want to do and places I want to see before I die. These things have pushed me to the edge and have tested my sanity and commitment, and have made me a stronger person. My parents are my greatest supporters, and the love that my family shares, as well as the overall outgoing nature, and freedom that I have gained from my parents have helped shaped me as well.

When I left high school, I was at a stage where I had just finished fitting in. I spent the summer trying to figure out exactly who I was, and as I enter college now I know who I am. I am a beatnik kid from northeast Ohio with a love of horses, and who does unconventional things sometimes. I love my life, and I will always hold true the things that have shaped me, such as my hobbies, my high school and my love of hard work and nature. Life is crazy, and I will always be tested in my values, but my integrity as a person will never change. I will continue on pushing the limits of others and myself and always working hard to make sure that I am genuine in my character, and not conforming to normality and instead continuing down my own beatnik path.

Project 1 Essay: I am a Valkyrie

CIS 110

6 October 2011

Valkyrie Pride

I spent the best, most rewarding and insightful four years of my life as a student at Sacred Heart Academy, but I did not know it yet. Sacred Heart is an all-girls Catholic high school in Louisville, Kentucky. I entered the doors as a freshman without even realizing the journey I was embarking on toward my future. Four years later I graduated as a completely different person. Sacred Heart Academy made me into the woman that I am today and what my experience there taught me will continue to benefit me for the rest of my life. Sacred Heart made me a Valkyrie.

Now at this point most people's first question is, "What in the world is a Valkyrie?" but I will get to that later. I want to start off talking about who I was before my time at Sacred Heart changed my life. I am the baby of my family, meaning that I have always gotten the attention. I have an older sister and two cousins that are more like siblings, who have always kept a close eye on me. This close eye is with good reason; when I was very young I was that little girl that was always putting on a fashion show or dance recital for my family to watch. Fast-forward to about second grade and you would see a completely different girl. I started having trouble in school, which was something I had never seen my older siblings go through. Because of this my entire attitude changed. I went from being confident and out going to shy and self-conscious little girl. I did not have very many friends at school and I spent all of my free time riding and showing my horses. My mom, being a teacher, got me the appropriate help and by sixth grade I was academically well ahead of my classmates. But going through middle school with very few friends is not easy. I was teased more than I let anyone really know about and struggled through my middle school years. I counted down the days until I finally got to move on to Sacred Heart Academy.

For as long as I can remember I have had family members attending Sacred Heart. I spent my child hood listening to my sister and cousins share funny, sad, and heart warming anecdotes about their time as Sacred Heart students and I knew I wanted to be "a part of the heart."

My first experience inside the school was when I went to shadow my older sister, Maddie, as a seventh grader. I was so nervous and did not know what to expect. I had my sister pick out my outfit and do my hair to avoid looking like the typical, lame seventh grader. I perfectly remember walking in through the lobby and being stopped by the principal, Dr. Beverly McAuliffe, who told me how excited she was to have me in the building for the day. Walking through the hall way with my sister before school even started completely shocked me. All the girls were smiling, waving to me, and chatting with their friends, and it was only 7 a.m. I imminently felt what I had listened to my family talk about for so many years; I felt home. I went back to shadow Maddie three more times, the maximum amount allowed, over the next two years. Not because I had any question in my mind about where I wanted to attend high school, because I genuinely felt so good about myself every time I stepped in the doors at Sacred Heart Academy.

Finally, in August of 2007 it was my turn. My sister and cousins had all graduated and I was the last of my family to go through Sacred Heart. I put on my sisters old uniform and spent my first week smiling and nodding my head at the continually asked questions, "You're Maddie's little sister, aren't you?" I was still shy, and spent the beginning of my freshman year hiding in my sister's shadow. But things were changing; I was making friends and doing well in school.

It took me about a month at Sacred Heart to memorize Dr. McAuliffe's famous speech that she said over the announcements to the entire student body every Friday. It varied slightly, but went something like this: "Do nothing this weekend to harm your mind, body, or spirit. No sex, no drugs, no alcohol. I encourage you to go the church of your faith tradition this weekend. And above all be Valkyries, strong women of great faith." I heard this phrase countless times over my four years at Sacred Heart, but it was not until after I graduated that I truly understood what Dr. McAuliffe meant by a "strong woman of great faith."

Toward the end of my freshman year I decided I was going to make my own Sacred Heart experience, just like my sister and cousins did. I tried out to be a part of the Ambassador program, the most prestigious program on campus, and to my surprise I was selected. As an ambassador I traveled to Catholic grade schools where I talked to the girls about what a positive experience I was having at Sacred Heart and encouraged them to attend the school as well. Now when you are in high school talking to six, seventh, and eight grade girls is not very difficult because they hang off every word that you say. The real challenge comes with talking to their parents. Junior year the Ambassador director asked me to speak at Open House. This meant that I would be giving a speech to all perspective students and their parents. My first thought was, "there is no way I can talk in front of that many people." My second thought was, "how could I possibly put in to words what this school means to me?" But I did it. I wrote it. I practiced for hours on a five-minute speech, but I was still so nervous that I would not do the school justice in that short amount of time. As I was finishing my speech, I spotted my mom's best friend, in the crowd with her seventh grade daughter, wiping tears from her face. At that moment I knew I had pulled it off. She had watched me evolve from a timid pre-teen to a poised and confident young lady, all due to Sacred Heart's influence on me.

REVERENCE

Not only did Sacred Heart provide me with confidence, it provided me what I believe is the strongest academic and religious foundation that there is to offer. The vigorous academic standards that I was held to while at Sacred Heart have prepared me for college and the rest of my life. In addition to this, the religious foundations through daily prayer and retreats provided me with the tools and the relationship with God to be successful and faithful down any path my life takes me.

As a student at Sacred Heart I excelled in academics and in my religious faith, but I learned important lessons on the field as an athlete wearing a Sacred Heart uniform as well. All you have to do is take a look at the state championship banners around the gym and it is clear that Sacred Heart has a strong tradition of athletic excellence. Freshman year I tried out for the lacrosse team and made junior varsity. We had fun, but did not win very often, which is unacceptable while wearing a Sacred Heart Valkyrie jersey. Sophomore year was my first time on a varsity team, which was much more challenging. For the remainder of my time at Sacred Heart my team was the underdog. We had a great group of girls with a lot of athletic talent and we decided we were going to make the most of it. For the next three years we worked year-around to be the best in the state. This taught me the true meaning of hard work, dedication, and teamwork. We ran countless suicides, spent time in the weight room, pushed through injuries, and finally my senior year we won Sacred Heart's first lacrosse state championship, going in as the underdog. It was the best feeling in the world to have the entire student body, teachers, staff, and parents rush the field after a game and three hard-fought overtimes.

The state championship game was on Thursday, May 19, 2011 quickly followed by graduation on Saturday, May 21, 2011. It was during this short time span that that it hit me more than ever: these people had become my family and this school had become my home. I made friendships with girls that will undoubtedly be my future bridesmaids. I made memories that I will cherish for the rest of my life. I gained 212 new sisters. I was part of a 135 year tradition, and joining the ranks of thousands of accomplished and respected Valkyries that had graduated before me, as shown in this picture. But I did not want to leave. I spent the day leading up to graduation crying that my time was coming to a close. I would have stayed at Sacred Heart forever if they let me, but that is not what they had preparing me for the past four years. My time had come to an end, but not without being given the best gift I could have ever received. I received the gift of

being confident, well-rounded, outgoing, well-educated, faithful, hard working, and accomplished. I received the gift of being a Valkyrie for the rest of my life.

Project 1 Essay: I am a Knitter

"Putting the Pieces of My Identity Together"

The memory of sitting in my mother's pottery shop, admiring her craft, is crystalline. She would begin swiftly by kneading the pile of mud, and placing it on her wheel. Then, spinning the clay gracefully, she would sculpt the mire into the object she desired. The process of her work was flawless. The product from her kiln was no longer mud, but a ceramic piece. The art my mother formed sparked the desire in myself to create. The words once said by Jeanne de Vietinghoff reminds me of my mother, "Woman was born to create, in creating she becomes herself, accomplishing her destiny—to create is not merely to produce a work, it is to give out ones own identity," (Hanna, 2011). I believe these words are true. Knitting has enabled me to put together a large piece in my life. My identity has evolved as I claimed the role as a knitter and began creating with yarn.

I have always lived in an environment immersed in the arts. I use my mother's ceramics pieces everyday and they inspire me to be productive and imaginative. The mug displayed in the photo throughout this essay is one she threw on her wheel. Not only was I immersed by my mother's creativity but also by my family's crafty friends. One of the most influential friends was my brother's colleague, Erin. I began noticing her work during our winter break. She would sit, watching the traditional holiday movies, and

Photo by: Allyce Capps

knit. The idea of knitting has always interested me because it is creative and produces a piece one can use, similar to pottery. The needles Erin held would interlock loops of yarn together to form a patterned scarf. The sticks moved back and forth and my eyes followed, watching the craft. The coordination she displayed made the process seem effortless, but the concept seemed difficult. I couldn't understand how she was *knitting*. I desperately wanted to understand, and she agreed to teach me.

Holding the two, thick sticks in my hand seemed clumsy and controlling the flimsy yarn seemed impossible. I concentrated on mimicking her motions: back and around, under, around and through. I repeated the order until my hands felt an arthritic ache. I kept the needles going until my hands naturally mimicked her sequence. Intertwining the string, putting the pieces together and keeping to the template of my beginner scarf not only created frustration but also produced a sense of peace. The process of learning how to knit has taught me stay calm, even in frustrating environments. It has also taught me to keep a clear head in difficult situations. When I get discouraged with a school assignment, knitting allows me to take a break from the course content and clear my head. Overtime, my first scarf was finished, then a second, then a third. After Erin first taught me to knit, I started to desperately desire a more difficult weaving project.

While I was visiting Fayetteville, Arkansas, a hippie-like knitting store, Handheld, was introduced to me by one of my mother's artistic friends. I went inside; in awe, I realized I wasn't the only one who wanted a challenge. Several women sat around a small, oak circle table in the center of the room, knitting very difficult-patterned sweaters. Both walls surrounding the tables were filled with delicate, beautiful yarn on white, urban designed shelves. The identity these women formed through knitting seemed serene, artistic, and intelligent. One could see the women knew an awful lot about yarns and needles. The atmosphere in Handheld was both tranquil and naturally knowledgeable. In school, my depiction of knowledge was being forced, and in that room I realized art didn't transpire the same way. The knowledge seemed desirable. I wanted to know as much about knitting as the women in the store.

There are often times in my life that I don't reveal to others that I am a knitter. It's a hobby that I am neither ashamed of nor proud of. However, sometimes others would ridicule me about it. The two statements I often hear from my peers are that it's a grandma hobby and boring. These negative comments used to bother me. But, when I walked into Handheld, I realized that if these women were grandmas and boring, I wanted to be just that.

When the trip ended and I came back to my hometown, I started looking for a store similar to Handheld. I found a small store off of our down town area that had just opened called Red Bug. In my opinion, there are two types of knitters. There are knitters who sit at home and knit by themselves and those who enjoy going to stores, like Handheld, and knitting as a community. The idea that I can grow and learn from the woman around me is a social aspect that appealed to me. I was anxious to visit and to see if the woman who owned it would teach me further. Red Bug became my community. Red Bug's owner was poised and serene as she invited me into her store. Although it was filled with antiques instead of the circular oak table, it had the same atmosphere as Handheld. Delicate yarn filled the vintage shelves. Instead of being very hippie like Fayetteville's, it felt like a charming southern cottage. I became very familiar with Red Bug over the next year as Trudy, the owner, started to teach me more challenging designs and patterns. Her calm, patient qualities helped make the transition from basic to intermediate clothing a smooth one.

When I encounter other knitters like Trudy, I feel I can understand their personalities and lives better. The idea that they enjoy keeping their hands busy, even when relaxing, is a quality I can relate to. The concept that they enjoy creating lets me know about their personality and that it is similar mine. Most knitters I have met have calm personalities, similar to Trudy's or my mother's friends. Their attitudes towards knitting has motivated me to support others aspiring to be knitters. When I do reveal that I knit to someone who wants to learn, I have the ability to teach him or her. I have taught several others, including my mother, how to knit. The ability to teach loved ones about a subject I care about fulfills me. The prospect of them picking up the hobby and the character they will gain through knitting makes me thrilled for them. I visualize a knitter sitting at home, snuggling up on the couch and constantly moving their needles.

From the very first session, I formed an identity and changed the way I understood myself through knitting. The identity of a knitter didn't stem from the fact that I picked up needles and yarn, but from the mindset it put me in. If I believed that a knitter's identity came from the quality or the number of scarves or sweaters they created, I would never believe myself to be a knitter. I always feel like there is improvement that can be made, whether you are an amateur or expert. The feeling it provides when I keep my hands busy and my mind clear only materializes when I knit. The practice permits me to be idle while still having the satisfaction of being productive. Although I often get confused with the template's oddly worded instructions or mess up the pattern that I am trying to create, I still enjoy the challenge of the conflict. In the photograph below, one can see the template I was using for the pastel orange sweater. Every time I finish a session, I feel a sense of accomplishment because I know that I produced a piece of clothing.

Through the past couple years, several far more accomplished knitters than myself have given me encouragement to become more advanced. The same woman that introduced me to Handheld runs the Underground in Fayetteville's court square. Underground takes place in the basement of the courthouse

Photo by: Allyce Capps

and displays works of artists. Underground also puts on runway shows of local knitter's work. The clothing is not only intricate in design but also vast in size. The detail and time each knitter put into the model's clothing inspires me to be able to perform in that quantity and quality. The owner of Handheld uploads photos every week to her Facebook, motivating me to get to her advanced level of creativity. The thought of producing the quality of work she creates, inspires me to choose the more complex projects my instructor throws at me. My teacher at Red Bug, Trudy, always pushes me to take on projects that I don't believe I can handle. Every time I finish a complex project, I am grateful that she pushed me forward. In the photo above, she gave me the choice between the sweater I am knitting and a headband. Needless to say, I chose the more complex project because I knew she'd help me with her gentle guidance. These artists inspire me to become more like them, in their craft and also in their character.

The craft of knitting has impacted my character immensely. It has also allowed me to understand that no piece of work is perfect. Handmade items have imperfections, which gives them more beauty. Before learning how to knit, I looked at imperfections as flaws because of my perfectionist personality. Knitting has given me a role that granted me peace and relaxation, determination and inspiration. In the photograph below, one can see the whole picture. Each piece has made up my role as a knitter. Intertwining the string and putting to weave together has enabled me to piece together the formation of my identity.

Photo by: Allyce Capps

References

Hana. (2011, July 20). Inspire: They said it best. [Web log comment]. Retrieved from

Project 1 Outlines

FORMAL OUTLINE

Informative Speech of Personal Significance

Name: Courtney Baxter

Title: Life's a Game, Softball is Serious

INTRODUCTION

I. **Attention Catcher:** After breaking my finger 7 times, a busted lip, back spasms, multiple sprang ankles, and a concussion, I think it is safe to say softball is my passion.

II. **Listener Relevance Link:** For those of you who have played a sport I'm sure you can relate to losing a big game, not starting a game, and/or remembering the last game you played in your high school uniform.

III. **Speaker Credibility:** My Dad taught me to play softball when I was 6 years old. I started out playing in a coed league. This meant I had to be tough. I am always either playing or watching softball in the spring and summer. I always say all things that happen in one person's life happen in seven innings of a single softball game.

IV. **Thesis Statement:** Today I am going to tell you how being captain of my high school softball team changed my self-concept from quiet and shy to being a leader, role-model, and a sister.

V. **Preview:** I'll do this through 3 games. The Montgomery County Varsity game, The Montgomery County JV game, and the District game that ended our season against Clark County.

BODY

I. **First Main Point:** The Montgomery County Varsity game gave me an opportunity to be a leader.

   A. **Subpoint:** I had to be vocal and tell the girl's to be quiet and pay attention.

   1. **Sub-Subpoint:** Usually I wasn't the person to step up, but the girl's listened and almost too literally.

   2. **Sub-Subpoint:** Usually we cheer but the girl's were very quiet and not into the game.

   B. **Subpoint:** I had to start a cheer in order to show the girl's that being quiet didn't mean to be quiet.

   1. We started yelling and making noise which rattled the other team.

   2. We started to gain confidence because we were being supportive of our team.

Transition: Although Varsity games are important, JV games are just as important, because that is where the younger players learn new positions in case of a varsity injury.

II. **Second Main Point:** The Montgomery County JV game allowed me not only be a vocal leader but to show my leadership skills and bond with the girls.

Listener Relevance Link: Everyone in this room has faced the problem where they didn't want to stand up to others around them.

    A. **Subpoint:** I always got on the JV girls during the Varsity games for being disrespectful so it was only right to do so during the JV game.

        1. **Sub-Subpoint:** Respect goes two-ways

        2. **Sub-subpoint:** I told the girl's not to be messing around in the dugout during the JV games.

    B. **Subpoint:** I showed the girls I wanted the entire team to succeed not just the varsity.

        1. **Sub-Subpoint:** The girls knew they could confide in me and I wouldn't be bias whether it was a varsity or JV problem.

        2. **Sub-Subpoint:** We bonded because this new relationship and formed like a sisterhood.

Transition: Through all of this, we became a team; a team who could succeed. The most exciting, nerve-racking intense game that I did not play in was districts my senior year.

III. **Third Main Point:** Not playing in the district game allowed me to become a role model to the girls.

Listener Relevance Link: Most of us have had that moment where we've wanted nothing more but to one thing, and we'd give anything to do it.

    A. **Subpoint:** I was a team player, who supported the team.

        1. **Sub-Subpoint:** It was my senior year and I would've loved to play, but all I wanted was the team to succeed.

    B. **Subpoint:** I was captain, so it was even more difficult not to play because I was supposed to be a leader

        1. **Sub-subpoint:** Being Captain and still being able to suck it up and cheer the girl's on showed character and persuaded the girls' views of me.

        2. **Sub-subpoint:** The girl's seeing me as a role-model, allowed myself to see me as a role-model.

Transition: Softball was my way of life, and throughout my senior year I tried to be the captain I thought would lead us to victories.

CONCLUSION

I. **Restatement of Thesis:** Being softball captain changed my self-concept from shy and quiet to a leader, role-model and sister. Because the way the girl's viewed me allowed my way of seeing myself to change.

II. **Summary of Main point:** If it wasn't for my courage to change during the Montgomery County games and the district game then I feel as if my self-concept wouldn't have changed because the girl's wouldn't have seen me any differently than in the past few years and I wouldn't have seen myself differently.

III. **Clincher:** We all have that moment in life where we need to step out of our comfort zone, mine just so happened to be in something I loved. Will you step out of your comfort zone in order to help others succeed?

First Learned to Play

Front: Haley Wagner, Kandice, Destinee, Danielle, Shannon, Alyssa, Megan, Rachel, Katie Tubbs, Kristen, Stephanie Yazell
Back: Sadie, Stephanie Fredrick, Kassy, Katie Jacoby, Lindsey, Christina, Miranda, Karissa, Lauren Dawson, Jessica, Lauren Royse, Haylie Dennis, Me, Hannah

Montgomery Co. Victory

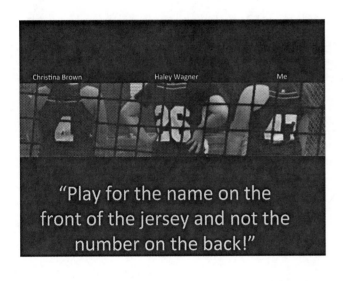

Christina Brown   Haley Wagner   Me

"Play for the name on the front of the jersey and not the number on the back!"

"Play for the name on the front of the jersey and not the number on the back!"

L to R: Coach Sosby, Christina Brown, Haley Wagner, Me

District Captains Meeting

FORMAL OUTLINE

NAME: _____ Kathleen Miller _____ **SECTION:** ____007____

TITLE OF SPEECH: _____ The Outdoors Woman _____

Be sure to label learning styles throughout.

INTRODUCTION

   I. **Attention Catcher:** Mt. Everest, the Great Barrier reef, the Grand Canyon…The list goes on and on. What do all of these things have in common? They are all part of nature.

   II. **Listener Relevance Link:** We all come into contact with nature everyday. Even though it might not be as magnificent as the ones I previously listed, nature is constantly around us.

   III. **Speaker Credibility:** I love the outdoors and have for as long as I can remember. I enjoy hiking, going to the lake, or any other activity outside.

   IV. **Thesis Statement:** My self concept affects other's perceptions of me because it demonstrates the importance of relationships, shows my personality, and showcases my hidden hobbies.

   V. **Preview:** First, I will mention why relationships are important to me and how my love for the outdoors has affected that.

Transition (optional):

BODY

   I. **First Main Point:** Relationships

Listener Relevance Link: We all have various relationships in our lives, whether they are with our immediate family, relatives, or a group of friends, relationships are still an important part of our lives.

   A. **Subpoint:** Being an outdoors woman has really affected my relationship with my family for the better. By doing activities outdoors with them, we have grown closer.

   1. **Sub-Subpoint:** I always go hiking with my dad. My sister also comes most of the time, but my dad always goes with me. While hiking, we have time to talk about various things that we wouldn't get to talk about if we were back "in the real world." Since it is just us out in the woods without any distractions.

   2. **Sub-Subpoint:** Another example is when my family goes down to the lake. My dad takes my sister and I out fishing, tubing, and water skiing during the day. We go down

to the lake once or twice a year. Again, this is a vacation where we can just spend time with each other.

B. **Subpoint:** My self concept has also bettered my relationship with God.

   1. **Sub-Subpoint:** When I go hiking, there is not much to do besides walk along the path and look at all the trees. So, I have some time where I can pray to God. I can talk with Him about what is going on in my life or just have a conversation.

   2. **Sub-Subpoint:** Also, when I am hiking, I can take the time and appreciate all of the things that God created. I am more thankful for everything he created as I am walking and can actually see the creations.

Transition: In addition to my relationships, others can perceive my personality through my self concept of the outdoors woman.

II. **Second Main Point:** My personality

Listener Relevance Link: We all have varying personalities, but some aspects of my personality can be seen through my love for the outdoors.

A. **Subpoint:** One aspect of my personality is that I am a simplistic person, meaning that I am content with just being outside.

   1. **Sub-Subpoint:** An example is how I enjoy hiking. When I am hiking through the woods, I don't need anything except a backpack full of supplies. It is a very a low key activity and doesn't require complicated equipment. I can just sit back and enjoy the scenery.

   2. **Sub-Subpoint:** Another example is riding my bike. One of my favorite things to do is to ride my bike around my neighborhood. Even though it may seem boring, I really enjoy it. I love riding my bike whenever I get the chance to. It is a chance to exercise and have fun at the same time.

B. **Subpoint:** Another aspect of my personality that comes across through my self concept is patience.

   1. **Sub-Subpoint:** The first example that comes to mind is when I am hiking, it sometimes can take awhile to get to the destination. I don't mind the long hikes because I can spend more time with my family or admiring the landscape.

   2. **Sub-Subpoint:** Something else that requires a lot of patience is fishing. This is an extremely slow sport if the fish aren't biting. However, my patience really comes through when we are just sitting on the boat for a couple of hours without even getting a bite. I still love fishing even though it isn't always the most exciting thing to do.

Transition: Just as my personality can be seen through my self concept, so can some of my hidden hobbies.

III. **Third Main Point:** Hidden hobbies

Listener Relevance Link: I know we all have things about us that people would know as soon as they met us, but other qualities would be harder to know based on a first encounter.

    A. **Subpoint:** Since I am a reserved person, and don't enjoy thrill rides, most people would correctly assume that I would not like adventurous water sports.

        1. **Sub-Subpoint:** One of my hidden hobbies is water skiing. However, this shouldn't come as a shock if people knew my self-concept. They might actually think differently about this. I learned how to ski 2 years ago and have been doing it ever since.

        2. **Sub-Subpoint:** Another thing I love to do is go tubing at the lake. Even though tubing to some may not seem that adventurous, compared to my quiet and reserved personality, it is very outgoing.

    B. **Subpoint:** Another aspect about me that most people would not assume is true is that I like going to new places.

        1. **Sub-Subpoint:** When I am hiking, I like to hike to specific formations or new attractions that I have never seen. I think that this makes the trip more enjoyable if I am able to witness something new.

        2. **Sub-Subpoint:** Another example is when I was with my dad and I went to Red River Gorge and we climbed Indian Staircase. It is giant rock that has hand holes carved out of it by the Indians, and used as a staircase to reach the top of the ridge. My dad and I decided to climb it one hiking trip. It was extremely steep and scary. I had never climbed it before, so it was a brand new experience that definitely drew me out of my comfort zone.

Transition: My hidden hobbies just one of the many parts of my self concept.

CONCLUSION

    I. **Restatement of Thesis:** The Outdoors woman concept affects others' view me because it shows my love of relationships, reflects my personality, and showcases my hidden hobbies.

    II. **Summary of Main Points:** Others can perceive that through my love of the outdoors, relationships are important to me. Specifically, doing things outdoors have brought my family closer together, and has brought me closer to God. Also, aspects of my personality such as simplicity and patience, can be seen through my self concept. Finally, I have many hidden hobbies such as water skiing and tubing, and also exploring new areas.

    III. **Clincher:** So the next time you look outside and only see a tree or a bird, just think about all the possibilities the outdoors could offer you.

FORMAL OUTLINE

NAME: _____ Jeffrey Key_____ SECTION: _____001_____

TITLE OF SPEECH: _____ My Impact as a Hunter_____

Be sure to label learning styles throughout.

INTRODUCTION

I. **Attention Catcher:** Do you know what it is like to wonder if you will be able to afford food to serve at your dinner table during the holidays?

II. **Listener Relevance Link:** Most people in this classroom have never been in the situation having to wonder where their next meal will come from. But for many this is a daily worry.

III. **Speaker Credibility:** For over five years now I have helped to lessen this worry among the under privileged by providing meat to them for the holidays.

IV. **Thesis Statement:** A hunter provides for his family and friends.

V. **Preview:** Being a hunter means being a provider, being a leader, being a friend, determined, and a jack of all trades.

Transition (optional): A hunter provides for his family with the support of god and his friends.

BODY

I. **First Main Point** I, as a hunter, am a man of integrity that provides and cares for my family.
Listener Relevance Link: Every family has a member that the family members know that they can go to for help in times of need and support.

    A. **Subpoint:** At a young age I was forced to grow up and assume the role as the man of the house when my dad left.

        1. **Sub-Subpoint:** I had to take care of the home and my sister and mom.

        2. **Sub-Subpoint:** Many people commented on how mature I was and what integrity I must have to be able to do that at such a young age.

    B. **Subpoint:** Most of my block consist of elderly and I am frequently called upon to take care of them.

        1. **Sub-Subpoint:** During the ice storm I removed trees form the elderly's yards, built them fires to stay warm, back wired their furnaces to generators all before I tended to heating my house.

2. **Sub-Subpoint:** I made such an impression by tending to the elderly before my self that I received many letters of recommendation for college mentioning my integrity and maturity.

Transition: Part of helping others is being thankful for what god has given you in life.

II. **Second Main Point** Being a Hunter has taught me to be thankful for what I am given.
Listener Relevance Link:

A. **Subpoint:** Being able to harvest an animal is a very spiritual experience that calls for a time of thanksgiving and family gathering.

1. **Sub-Subpoint:** Every time I harvest an animal, my family comes together to give thanks and then process the animal.

2. **Sub-Subpoint:** Once the thanks has been given and the meat has been blessed we share a family meal in celebration. It is experiences like these that lead my family to be so tightly knit.

Project 2 Essay: The Baptist Community

The Baptist Community

Kathleen Miller

University of Kentucky

CIS 110 Section 007

Allyson DeVito

November 28, 2011

Abstract

The Baptist community is a denomination of the Christian religion. In order to better understand this community, I decided to observe Immanuel Baptist Church. During the course of exploring the Baptist denomination, I was able to learn more about their emphasis on serving others. Also, reaching out to the college-aged students is another major focus of the Baptist community and Immanuel Baptist Church. Due to my exposure to the Baptist community, I now have a better understanding of a different Christian denomination.

Christianity-one religion, many denominations. This idea can be confusing to someone, especially if they are not Christian. There are many different denominations of Christianity such as Catholic, Baptist, Methodist, Presbyterian, and the list goes on. I was raised Catholic and now go to a non-denominational Christian church. Due to this, I have never had much exposure to the Baptist denomination of the Christian faith. I was very interested in learning about a different Christian denomination, since I went to Catholic grade school and high school. It was a chance for me to explore another denomination within the Christian faith when I otherwise would not have had the same opportunity. I was just curious to see in what ways the Baptist community differed from the Catholic community. Specifically, I wanted to learn what the Baptist services were like and what they taught. By observing and being involved in the Baptist community, I have learned different aspects of this Christian denomination and the ways in which they spread their faith.

When I first started exploring the Baptist community, I was not really sure what I was expecting. Before I began researching my community, I had a few ideas in my mind of what I thought a Baptist service would be like. I thought that everything would be very traditional, proper, and strict. My stereotypes probably stem from the media and how they portray the Baptist community. However, I am not the only one to have these preconceived notions about the Baptist denomination. According to Nathan Cornett who works as the college and missions pastor for Immanuel Baptist Church, some of the major stereotypes are that Baptists can be seen as "judgmental" and "old-fashioned" (Cornett, Personal Interview, 2011). Despite my previous thoughts about the Baptist community, I set everything aside so I could be open to this new Christian denomination that I knew little about.

I went to Immanuel Baptist Church in Lexington in order to learn more about the Baptist community. According to Cornett, "Immanuel is a Southern Baptist church, and that means that we partner with other churches that are in the Southern Baptist Convention" (Cornett, Personal Interview, 2011). Cornett goes on to say "it's a denomination that is basically put together so that we can help send missionaries, and we can partner together as independent churches to help take the message of Jesus Christ around the world" (Cornett, Personal Interview, 2011). The Southern Baptist Convention began in the year 1845, and today is made up of over 40,000 churches nationwide ("About Us-Meet Southern Baptists," 2011). The first president of the

Southern Baptist Convention was Dr. W. B. Johnson (Barnes, 1954). By doing research through Immanuel Baptist Church, I have gained knowledge regarding the Baptist denomination that I would have never known.

Photo taken by Kathleen Miller

One of the first things I learned was the style of the Baptist service. I was able to attend Sunday morning church services. The service was completely different from the Catholic mass. The worship leader started off the service by leading everyone in more contemporary praise songs. Following the worship, the preacher gave his sermon. Another observation I had was that many of the church members brought their Bibles to church so that they could follow along with the preacher. Some of these aspects of Immanuel Baptist Church are similar to the church I attend now, but completely different from my Catholic background.

In addition to the service, I learned that the Baptist community strives to reach out to help others in need. On a Wednesday night when I attended the college bible study, Immanuel was hosting something called Room in the Inn. According to Cornett, it is a program for homeless people (Cornett, Personal Interview, 2011). On Wednesday night, homeless men come into the church and are fed dinner and given a place to stay the night ("Missions and Outreach"). According to Cornett, their service opportunities are "ways to help people grow closer to Christ" (Cornett, Personal Interview 2011).

Photo taken by Kathleen Miller

Another way that Immanuel is trying to improve the community is through the creation and delivery of Thanksgiving baskets. It is a chance to reach out to people in the Lexington area who may not be able to make Thanksgiving dinner possible. Volunteers packed boxes full of Thanksgiving dinner necessities and delivered them to the people. I was lucky enough to be able to help out with the delivery. Our group was in charge of hand delivering the Thanksgiving baskets to specific residents in a few apartment complexes near Immanuel. As I delivered these baskets, the gratitude I received from the people made it all worthwhile. Just knowing that I was doing God's work and helping out those less fortunate really made an impact on me. All of the other college volunteers that were in my group were also very excited to be there and spread the love of God. This event was just another example of how service is a very top priority in the Baptist community, and specifically at Immanuel Baptist Church. In addition to understanding how the Baptist denomination reaches out to needy people in the community, I have learned how they reach out to college-aged students.

Having college students being a part of a church can be sometimes difficult because of lack of time to sheer apathy. However, the Baptist community is making strides in order to connect college students to Christ and get them involved in the church. Since Nathan Cornett is the college pastor, he says that, "I am charged with seeing that college students grow closer, take that next step, whatever that might be, closer to Christ" (Cornett, Personal Interview, 2011). One way that Immanuel reaches out to college students is through their Wednesday night worship. I was able to attend one of these Wednesday worship nights, and I thoroughly enjoyed it. The worship was held in a small room in the church, and about twenty-five college students came. They began the evening with singing praise and worship songs. Then Nathan Cornett presented a mini sermon about loving God and each other. He related the sermon to lives of college-aged students so that we could more easily understand and apply it. Upon completion of speaking, the worship leaders led the students in a few more praise songs. After he had

Photo taken by Kathleen Miller

finished, the singers sang a few more songs. Even though it was not a huge production or very crowded, I still felt the presence of God there. I could genuinely see that Immanuel was trying to reach out to college students.

Another way Immanuel Baptist Church is reaching out to the college students is through their contemporary service. Cornett said that this service is called "Pulse," and it is geared toward the "younger generation." He also said that the music played is "closer to what we are hearing on radio stations today" (Cornett, Personal Interview, 2011). I have attended two of the contemporary services at Immanuel in order to gain more understanding of the Baptist community. It is definitely a more modern worship service because of the current music. The experience resembled a concert because of all the guitars, singers, drums, and lights. I found that this was a great to draw in college students. Also, the sermon was very relatable, and it was delivered in such a way so that anyone could understand. After the service is over, Cornett leads a Sunday school for the college students. The topic discussed does not necessarily relate to the sermon given, but it still sends out a message that is relatable to college Christians. The Sunday school was a very relaxed and interactive environment, and everyone was sitting in a circle listening to Cornett discuss a certain Bible passage. It was a great way for college students to connect with each other in a Christian environment.

Working with the Baptist community has really affected me personally in many ways. First of all, I have realized that I need to be serving others more than I have been. I like volunteering, it is just hard to set aside time to do so. However, by going to Immanuel Baptist Church, I have been given many options to help serve in the Lexington community. Another aspect of this community that has affected me is the fact that college students are actively participating in their Christian faith. It gives me hope that even though I live on a very religiously diverse college campus, there are still students that want to put Jesus first. In addition, by going to observe the services and other events, I have realized that I want to take my faith a step further. When I went to the services, I noticed that many people in the congregation had brought their Bibles into church. I had never really thought about this before, and would now like to do so. Finally, I have a new understanding of the Baptist denomination. I was able to see first hand a Baptist church, and from that I can see the denomination in a new light. The old stereotypes I previously had were proved wrong, especially the ones about the Baptist community being very strict and by the book. I now know, that at least with Immanuel Baptist Church, they are trying to be more modern to attract young people, and they have fun worshiping.

Since this community has affected me so much, I think that I will still continue to be a part of it. I do not think that I will officially switch to the Baptist denomination or join Immanuel Baptist Church, but I will still be involved while I am here at UK. I will continue to try and go to church there on Sundays and participate in Immanuel's volunteer opportunities. Every time I go there, I learn something new about Jesus, and I want to continue to learn more. I also like their style of worship and how they refer to the Bible so much. Therefore, I still want to participate in this particular Baptist community.

Over the past couple of weeks as I have been intently studying the Baptist community, and I have had many different realizations regarding their take on Christianity. At the beginning, I had some ideas pop into my head when someone would mention a Baptist, but through this project, I have learned to set those stereotypes aside. The Baptist community is very involved with their surrounding community. Immanuel hosts a variety of volunteer opportunities in order to help others who may be in need. The Baptist community is also very involved in trying to reach out to the college students in the area. Immanuel Baptist Church is doing this through all of their college geared bible studies and worship services. This community has definitely left an imprint on me, and I have changed for the better by the experience. Now that I have observed a different aspect of Christianity, I can allow myself to understand the slight differences between the denominations. Through this study, I have learned that even though the Christian faith has many denominations, the important thing is that they are all Christian.

References

About Us- Meet Southern Baptists. (n.d.). 2011. Retrieved 20 November 2011, from
    http://www.sbc.net/aboutus/default.asp

Barnes, W. W. (1954). *The Southern Baptist Convention 1845-1953.* Nashville, TN: Broadman Press.

Cornett, Nathan (13 November 2011). Personal Interview. *Baptist Community.*

Missions and Outreach. (n.d.). Retrieved 17 November 2011, from
    http://www.ibc-lex.org/#/connect/missions-outreach

Project 2 Essay: UK Choirs

Diversity in UK's Choirs

Eric Shockey

CIS 110-201

There are many groups and communities in society that exemplify a diverse part of culture. Any aspect of life that is different than the norm can be represented in a community, and usually one that is organized. There are communities based on things like race, ethnicity, religion, sexual orientation, and social class. Many of these even have a presence via student or faculty run organizations here at the University of Kentucky. There are also, however, groups on this campus that cater to unique interests, and because of this, offer interesting and distinctive combinations of basic cultural categories. My goal in this project was to place myself in one of these rather unusual groups, discover what diversities exist, and see things the way other people might see them. I did this by attending and observing certain groups in the choir program that the University of Kentucky offers.

I have never been in a choir group before, as I don't really think of myself as much of a singer outside of being in my car by myself. The closest thing to firsthand experience I have of choirs is watching my grandmother sing every Sunday in the small choir my church had as I was growing up. This choir, aside from not being very good, did not exemplify the diversity that I am currently looking for either, as it contained mostly old white ladies and men. The choirs that I feel offer a sort of community and organization that is different from the culture I experience are ones that are associated with schools and universities. These choirs pull in students from different walks of life from my own, and mix them together based on one special interest and talent.

My assumptions of university choir members were largely based on stereotypes and generalizations. I sort of expected serious choir people to be weird glee club singers, like this:

This is a picture of course of some of the cast from the TV show Glee,

and represents the sort of typecast people have with choir singers: a group of people who are not what would be considered 'normal.' Whether that means people of a different race, homosexual people, or even people of different social classes. I came to observe my first choir practice ready to see a room full of these sorts of people. I didn't realize what sort of surprise I was in for though.

In choosing which choir or choirs to observe and research, I asked my cousin, who is in the Men's Chorus on campus. My cousin is not really in a different sort of social category than I am, so I was curious to see what his experience was like. He told me that the most diversity would probably be in the Men's Chorus and the Women's Choir, because these two choirs are open to all students on campus, not just students of the School of Music. I was intrigued; I wanted to know if the Music majors who were no doubt strange people, drew all of the other strange people from across campus to join the choirs. Plus, I would get to at least experience a women's organization, which is one group that I am not a part of.

I went to a **Men's Chorus** rehearsal first. Men's Chorus and Women's Choir are not exactly extracurricular activities like some of campus' student organizations or things like sports are; they are actually classes that meet Tuesdays and Thursdays and are worth one credit hour per semester. This is something of a misnomer though; as these are not like any class I've ever taken. The Men's Chorus meets in a large room in the basement of the Fine Arts building that has a stepped down floor with folding chairs on each platform. This room was clearly designed to be a rehearsal room rather than a classroom, as there was space for the 70 or so members of the choir to sit and face the back of the room where the piano and conductor would be located. Beyond just how different the room was, I was struck by how different the atmosphere was. Everyone seemed to get to class ten minutes early, more or less to just socialize with each other, as they all seemed to be friends. This is unlike any class I've ever taken outside of my major, where everyone's goal seems to be to spend as little time in the room and with each other as possible.

The diversity I found in the class made the atmosphere even more interesting. It was obvious that some people in the class were rather old, probably graduate students, while there were still many others that appeared to be freshmen or sophomores. And, surprising to me because I had never really considered race to be a large factor, probably about one third of the 70 choir members were African American. The more I thought about the obvious diversity, the more it impressed me. I thought about it in comparison to, for example, my fraternity meetings, where I look around and for the most part everyone is a freshman or a sophomore, white, and dresses similarly. This group had guys that that wore jeans and sweatshirts or things like that, while others, for instance, may be noticeably dressed up, or may have noticeably long hair, and things along those lines.

The actual rehearsal was also fairly strange, especially compared to normal classes. When two o'clock came around, Dr. Jefferson Johnson, who conducted the choir, simply stood up on his chair (using it as a sort of makeshift conductor's platform) and hummed one note loudly until the whole choir began humming with him. Warm-ups started from this humming, and as warm-ups progressed I noticed everyone was organized into one of the four vocal sections of the choir (tenor 1, tenor 2, baritone, and bass). After warm-ups Dr. Johnson spoke for a minute about the upcoming Christmas Collage concert the choir will be singing in, and then went about rehearsing songs.

In an interview I conducted with Men's Chorus member Neal Donhoff, he discussed a little bit about the atmosphere of the class: "It's definitely the most unique class I've taken. It's more relaxed than getting a lecture, and it's pretty fun a lot of the time too. I don't think of it as a class as much, because my other classes have tests and other things that I dread or don't want to do. I always like going to choir, and we are rewarded with concerts instead of tests."

Aside from the class's environment, Mr. Donhoff also commented on the sort of diversity present in the choir. He commented on the age difference present, as I discussed before, as some members were perusing their masters in the College of Music, while others, like Mr. Donhoff, were undergraduate students. He also mentioned the racial diversity, though he commented on the choir's cohesiveness as no one sees race as a cause for difference. Interestingly as well, he spoke of another alternative community present in the choir: "There are also quite a few homosexual people in it to, which is I guess a stereotype about guys who sing in choirs." The presence of this diversity I believe makes the Men's Chorus a unique community in itself, as very few organizations offer such racial, sexual, and age diversity, let alone in such an intimate setting.

The Men's Chorus, beyond being no doubt one of the most unique groups on campus, is also very successful. They've received recent honors of being the only Men's Chorus in the

country to be invited to prestigious events, such as the Music
Educators National Conference
Convention in Salt Lake City
and the inaugural convention of
the National Collegiate Choral
Organization (UK Men's Chorus
Page, 2011), and in 2007 were
named ahead of such prestigious
choirs as the Harvard Glee Club
and the University of Michigan
Glee Club as one of a select few
most premier university men's
choir in the nation. Below is a
photo of the choir performing in

one of their concerts, in which you can see a soloist standing alongside Dr. Johnson with the rest
singing in the background. I really like the professionalism they present in all members wearing
tuxedos. I had a vague idea before starting this project that they might sing and dance in ridicu-
lous outfits, as I again based some generalizations on stereotypes like those seen in Glee.

The determination that the Men's Choir seems to function more like a club than a class
seems to be rooted in the history of such groups. In Leonard Van Camp's essay (1965) analyzing
the formation of choral groups at certain colleges, he explains the intent of choirs. They were at
first not meant to be classes, as many universities years ago did not have colleges in which to get
a degree in music. These were mainly clubs and groups that assembled outside classes. In some
schools, glee clubs were among the first extracurricular activities to be established. This spirit
continues today, as the function of the choirs I observed is more a club or group than a class.

That Thursday, I visited a rehearsal of the University of Kentucky's **Women's Choir**. The
Women's Choir is larger than their counterpart, as they have about 100 members, and they
therefore must meet in the Singletary Center, where many of the Music and Theater Programs'
performances take place. They practice in a large room that is part of the backstage area, and

is filled with a semicircle of chairs. Much like the Men's Chorus, many of the Women's Choir members came to class early to socialize, as groups of them appeared to be very good friends. Dr. Lori Hetzel is their conductor, and she runs the choir's rehearsals in much the same spirit as Dr. Johnson does. The intent is to create a comfortable atmosphere in which choir members can sing and enjoy themselves. It is noticeable, however, that the diversity isn't as pronounced as it is in the Men's Choir. The Men's Chorus includes 25 or 30 African Americans out of 70 members, whereas the Women's Choir has only around 10 African Americans out of 100 members. The diversity within the group is instead focused on drawing a large number of students from around campus. The Men's Chorus appears to have many Music majors supplemented by a good amount of interested students from around campus. The Women's Choir, though, draws a very large percentage of its members from different backgrounds (UK Women's Choir, 2011).

The Women's Choir for me however offered a glimpse into a community that I am not a part of. This is of course a different gender group, as obviously all members, along with the conductor and the accompanying pianist, are women. This left me in the position of being the only male in the room when I was observing their rehearsal that Thursday.

I didn't really know what to expect in regards to facing the new experience of being in a room with over one hundred women, but I had a feeling it would probably be a little different that what I experience at the Men's Chorus rehearsal. It was a little different in the way it felt to me, though in looking at it objectively it was much the same. The girls socialized with each other in much the same way as the guys did, and as I explained before the rehearsal was much the same. I suppose it perhaps seemed a little different as I mention because I would be more likely to be comfortable socializing in a large group of only guys than I would in a large group of only girls. Suffice it to say that in my own mind I was very aware of being the only male in the room, whereas I could consider myself as one of everyone else in the Men's Chorus. Another aspect that may have only been in my own mind as well was that I sort of perceived some more animosity or perhaps even drama within the Women's Choir that I did not feel in the Men's Chorus. This I didn't really notice in the practice, but when I attended the Music Program's **Christmas Collage**, during which I spent some time backstage with the choirs, I did pick up on it more. This animosity appeared to manifest in the differences of singing parts. The singing parts in the Women's choir are Soprano 1 (the highest singers), Soprano 2, Alto 1, and Alto 2 (the lowest). The Altos in general appear to not be very fond of the Sopranos, who generally get the lead parts, and vice versa. The groups tend to segregate from each other, and in stressful times, such as during the collage, tensions can run high and rather straight forward and unpleasant can be at sometimes made. I do not know if this is just a product of having that many girls needing to cooperate in taxing situations or if it is a situation that is more unique. Either way, I counted this as an experience that I am relatively unfamiliar with, and one that seemed to be rather pervasive in this community.

I interviewed from the Women's Choir soprano Lisa Maxon, a senior Music Education major. She spoke, as Mr. Donhoff did, about how much she like Women's Choir compared to the other classes she had to take. Her other classes, like many students' classes from other majors around campus, are much more difficult. She also spoke of the closeness she had with some in the choir, specifically those who were also music majors, comparing it to the closeness she has with her friends in her sorority: "It sort of has more to do with being a music major, but I have pretty much two sets of friends: my sorority friends and my music friends. I usually spend more free time with my sorority friends but I go out with my music friends a lot too." Along with being in the Women's Choir, Lisa is the captain of a group called Paws and Listen. Paws and Listen is an a cappella group of women singers that includes a dozen of the best vocalists from the Women's Choir (the Men's Chorus has a similar sort of small elite group called the Acousticats). I noticed during the Christmas Collage that the sort of drama and fussiness present in the Women's Choir can be much more pronounced in this smaller group. This I assume is because Paws and Listen is student run and has no overseeing professor, so disagreements about things like song selection happen more. Below is a picture of

Paws and Listen in action. Ms. Maxon is the second from the left. Notice that the women also dress professionally when performing, as in the choirs the focus is on the singing not what the singers are wearing.

I believe I learned a great deal about different intercultural communities by observing the choirs of the University of Kentucky. And, most valuably, beyond only observing people of different genders, races, and sexual orientations, I got to see how these groups of people can come together and interact with each other in a successful way. The choirs do not function as classes where students come and go without a second thought; these are organizations in which students must cooperate. This can sometimes be challenging for various reasons, but the cohesiveness in spite of the diversity is what is impressive. I feel that I am richer for the experience now that I have been on the other side of cultural groups I had not been a part of.

Bibliography

Van Camp, L. (1965). The Formation of A Cappella Choirs. *Journal of Research in Music Education.* (13.4). 227-238.

University of Kentucky School of Music. (2011). UK Men's Chorus. Retrieved from http://www.uky.edu/ FineArts/Music/ensembles/menschorus/

University of Kentucky School of Music. (2011). *UK Women's Choir.* Retrieved from http://www.uky.edu/ FineArts/Music/ensembles/womenschoir/

Project 2 Essay: Kids' Café

Kids Café

Brittani M. Troutman

University of Kentucky

Composition and Communication 110, Section 047

Dr. Sarah Kercsmar

December 01, 2011

Abstract

Kids Café is an after school program for children in a lower class neighborhood about ten minutes from the University of Kentucky campus. Children go to Kids Café for a free meal and get help with homework. That community is much different than the community at UK. In this essay I explain my experiences at Kids Café and compare that to what I experienced as a kid and even now. There are two interviews in the essay that are from people who work at Kids Café that explains Kids Café and what it is. The purpose of the paper is to explain how the community of Kids Café is different from mine.

Kids Café

As I traveled ten minutes from campus to **Kids Cafe** I didn't pay much attention to my surroundings until I turned onto Seventh Street. I felt like I had entered a different world. I was expecting a nice building that would look somewhat like a daycare. I saw people walking around from place to place, which was normal to me, but what had changed and made this place different from my campus community, was the houses, cars, and how the people interacted with each other. Houses were tiny and beat up, cars were old, and as soon as I got out of the car, people started yelling at each other from the one side of the street to the other. I knew then I was in a different community. From that point on I would get to know a different social class then mine and start to understand the difference between the lower class and middle class.

Before I went to Kids Café, I thought it was going to be kind of like a daycare, with a nice building, many workers, and children that come from a poorer community. I expected the children's parents to be out of the picture and that many would be African American. I didn't think that Kids Café would be right in the middle of the lower class community like it is. I also thought that the children would have trouble in school and need extra help to keep up in school. What I found is that almost all my assumptions were wrong. During my first trip to Kids Café, I was very uneasy. I was in a totally different environment then I live in and wasn't sure about everything going on around me. The longer I was there, the more at ease I became, but I never really relaxed completely. The neighborhood around Kids Café was much different than the Lexington I was used to.

Kids Café is at the corner of Elm Tree Lane and East Seventh Street in a beat-up green building that used to be the Green Lantern Bar and Grill. You can see what the building looks like in this picture of the front of the building here in the middle. You can't see it well in the picture, but there is a sign that says children eat here for free. It is one of many Kids Cafés in the Lexington. It is a place where children from this neighborhood

Picture taken by me on November 20, 2011

can come and get help with homework, play with friends in a safe environment, and most of all get a free meal for dinner. Without this place, some of the children may not get to eat at night. When you first walk in, you can smell food being cooked in the kitchen. This Kids Café is one of the only ones in Lexington that makes their food and doesn't just open a can. Upstairs is a room where there are tables for children to do homework, play games, or read. On the back wall there is a big book shelf full of books. In the corner of the room there are shelves full of games. Also on the back wall is a nice TV. If you go up another flight of stairs you will find the computer room that has computers that the children can play games on or work on homework. All of these make Kids Café a very welcoming place.

The history of Kids Café is a very surprising one. The building started out as a bar and grill where the University of Kentucky and Transylvania University's teams coaches came to drink and hang out. After that shut down a church bought the building and decided to make it into a Kids Café in 1999. For two years, Kids Café was just a place for children to come and get a free meal. After a while, the people running the program decided that that was not enough so they decided that the children of the community needed more. So they started to not only offer the children food, but also an after-school program where the children could get help with homework and have a safe to play and be with friends. This Kids Café is one of the only ones in Lexington to make home-cook meals. They feed 15- 25 children each day (J. Koch, personal communications, November 20, 2011).

As soon as I walked into Kids Café, I was welcomed by many people and was directed to Jodie Koch, who is the person in charge of the program. Jodie has worked for Kids Café for four years and before that she volunteered there. She is the only full-time employee that works there, but she has two part-time employees that work with her also. When you walk in though you can see that there are plenty of volunteers. A lot of parents volunteer but most of the volunteers' come from the University of Kentucky. All the people at Kids Café, whether volunteers or employees, work hard for the children and try to make community a better place for the children, no matter what it takes. This was very clear when talking to Marie Eldridge. Marie is a part-time employee that has worked at Kids Café since it opened. When Marie was asked if there were any requirements to go to Kids Café, she said, "we will never turn a child away and not feed them for any reason." Marie has lived in the community for over 20 years and has been a part of Kids Café since it had opened in 1999. Marie told me her favorite part of working at Kids Café is working with and interacting with the children. Even though I only got to talk to two of the employees that work there, I knew just from talking to them that this was a passion for the workers. They loved their jobs and being able to make a difference in a community that didn't get much help from anyone else.

When the children get to Kids Café, there are many different activities for them to get involved in. One activity that they have every day is a book club. A person comes and reads them books. Right now they are reading *Harry Potter* series. The children really enjoyed listening and were very involved in the conversation after she was done reading. They asked many questions about things they didn't understand and the person reading the book would give them good examples that would make what was being read much clearer. During my first trip to Kids Café, the children learned about bullying. Nursing students from UK came and taught the children about why bullying is wrong and how to deal with or report it. Something that really surprised me about that activity was how much they knew about bullying. Even the younger children knew more than I had expected them to know. An activity like that is something that these children may never be exposed to if it wasn't for Kids Café. The workers at Kids Café give the children there a chance to use their imagination and learn life skills.

Children are the principal victims of poverty in the United States, where child poverty rates (defined as poverty among people under eighteen) are the highest in the industrial world (Appelbaum, Carr, Duneier, & Giddens, 2009). The neighborhood that people live in can often be a cause of their employment status and the poorer neighborhood the less likely there are jobs and more likely that people will be unemployed (Dujardin, & Goffette-Nagot, 2011). This makes it hard for the people living in communities like the one Kids Café is located in to find jobs and keep them long enough to get out of those communities. Programs like Kids Café make the lives of children in poverty and parents a little bit easier. They don't have to worry about a meal and can focus on other things. Fayette County alone has 6 different Kids Cafés and there are many others around the U.S. The rate of child poverty has a lot of factors. Of children under age eighteen living in poverty in 2004, 10.5 percent were white, 33.6 percent were black, 10 percent were Asian, and 28.9 percent were Hispanic; furthermore, 28.4 percent lived with single mothers (Appelbaum et al., 2009). I could see some of these factors while at Kids Café.

Most of the children there were African American. The picture to the left show some of the different races that where at Kids Café. It is very sad to see the number of children in poverty so high. But I am thankful Kids Café gives these children a place to go so they don't go to bed hungry. Also it is a place where children have an adult that they know they can rely on. The saddest part about children being in poverty is that they have no control over their finical situation. But with Kids Café helping the children in that community, they can grow up with the things they need to climb out of the class and make a better life for themselves. They can have a home away from home that helps them be better people. Growing up, I didn't have much and I often

Picture taken by me on November 20, 2011

moved for house to house, from the care of my grandma to the care of my mom. I saw a lot a young age that most children may not see ever in their lifetimes, but I never realized how much worse it could have been. For the most part I grew up in a lower middle class family. I always had food in my belly and never had to worry where my next meal was going to come from. While at Kids Café, the children there didn't have to worry about their needs. They were safe. I never knew how much I took just safety for granted. In the picture to the left you can see some of the volunteers cooking dinner for the children and enjoying themselves. The older woman in the picture cooks dinner there every night at Kids Café. She has for many years.

One thing that I noticed about the children at Kids Café is that they talked about violence. Some of the things they would say to each other I couldn't believe. One little boy told another, " I am going to cut your body into little pieces pour marinara sauce all over it and leave your head so you can eat it." The little boy was around four years old. It really made me think about how he learned to say things like that and what was between the lower class and the middle class that made us so different. I thought back to everything I have ever learned about the different classes and one thing stuck out to me the most. That was that lower class people often are involved in more crime. To them this makes things like crime and violence less of a big deal. They grow up around crime and this makes violence minor to them.

One thing that surprised me, but I thought was awesome about Kids Café, is how religiously based it is. The building is owned by a church and the food being used at Kids Café is donated by **God's Pantry Food Bank**. I believe having these things involved in Kids Café helps the children involved know God when they may not have any other way. This hits close to home for me because I didn't have a religious family. I grew up in a home where God was rarely mentioned. I may have never found my relationship with the Lord if it wasn't for a program I got involved in at a Daycare. The church down the road would come and pick us up and have activities and that taught us about the Lord. Without that church, I may have never decided to be saved. I feel that Kids Café can be a program for the children that are involved with it; like that church and Daycare were for me. I wouldn't be where I am today if I had never found that relationship with God, so to know that Kids Café is helping do that for other children means the world to me. Even if they don't know it God is working in their life.

Driving back to campus, I was still on edge. While at Kids Café, I had to watch my surroundings and keep a wall up to protect myself, because I was with people I have never met and in an environment that I had never been in. I have never had to watch my back in many communities that I have been in before. On campus, I am around people I don't know every day, but it is much different because I know I share similarities with those people. We all were going to school at UK or BCTC and about the same age. We all dress the same and talk the same. This was not the case at Kids Café. I was in a different community and I didn't know if I had similarities with the people there or not. But as I spent time with the people there, I found out that though we had many differences, but also had many similarities.

Going to Kids Café made me really think about the life I live. Just ten minutes down the road is a community that has it much harder than I have ever had it. I have complained about my little room in Blanding III and the same old food at Commons. I have even complained about my house back home that is having a lot of problems. But looking at it now I see how great my little house on the hill is. Now I think about how good I have it to have an opportunity to go to college and never have to worry about where I will sleep or what I am going to eat. I am blessed and I believe that Kids Café has blessed the children of that community. What they do for the children is priceless and I'm sure those children will remember that place forever. I will never forget the children at Kids Café.

References

Appelbaum, R., Carr, D., Duneier, M., Giddens, A. (2009) *Introduction to Sociology*. New York,   London: W.W. Norton & Company, Inc.

Dujardin, C., & Goffette-Nagot, F. (2011). Neighborhood effects on Unemployment?. *Regional Science and Urban Economics*, 40 (6), 380-396. doi:10.1016/j.regsciurbeco.2010.05.001

J. Koch, personal communications, November 20, 2011

M. Eldridge, personal communications, November 20, 2011

Project 2 Outlines

FORMAL OUTLINE INFORMATIVE SPEECH OF PERSONAL SIGNIFICANCE

NAME: Eric Shockey

TITLE: Diversity in UK's Choirs

INTRODUCTION

I. **Attention Catcher:** There are many different intercultural groups based on race, ethnicity, social class, religion, gender, and sexual orientation, and most of these have an organization on campus to be involved in. But there are also groups that cater to certain special interests or talents that may draw interesting combinations of cultural groups.

II. **Listener Relevance Link:** You may be a part of an organization that contains diversity like this, or you may even be a part of a different intercultural group. I am going to set out to see if the diverse groups can function by observing two of the student choir groups at UK

III. **Speaker Credibility:** I have never been in a choir before, and for the most part, the organizations on campus that I participate in do not have a great deal of diversity. So I will be unbiased and will be learning from this experience.

IV. **Thesis Statement:** The choir groups on campus include diverse groups of students, including many from different races, different ages, different sexualities, and different genders, but they have an impressive cohesiveness as they seem to not care about these differences

V. **Preview:** In this speech, I'll tell you about my assumptions before I observed the Men's Chorus and the Women's Choir and you'll be able to see how different they can be from the stereotypes.

Transition (optional):

BODY

I. **First Main Point** My assumptions before observing the choirs.
Listener Relevance Link: My assumptions I think went along with the sort of limited/stereotypical knowledge that most people possess for choirs.

    A. **Subpoint:** Based on choirs I know, I figured they'd be weird and eccentric.

        1. **Sub-Subpoint:** The closest to firsthand choir experience I have is watching my grandmother sing in the church choir, which wasn't diverse at all. It was mainly old white ladies and men.

2. **Sub-Subpoint:** I thought the choirs would probably be something like the show Glee, which includes a lot of 'not normal' people, as in people from different races, sexual orientations, and social classes.

B. **Subpoint:** I asked my cousin, who is in the men's chorus and in general isn't all that different from me, which choirs would be best to observe. He said the men's chorus and women's choir would be best because they're open to all students on campus not just music majors. I had different assumptions for each choir.

1. **Sub-Subpoint:** For the men's chorus, I expected there to be a bunch of different kinds of guys, which would lead them to be not cohesive. I base this on groups I have been in, such as my fraternity, in which were mostly the same, but we still don't always get along.

2. **Sub-Subpoint:** I had no idea what to expect for the women's choir, mainly because I haven't observed firsthand an all women's organization.

Transition: First I'll talk about the men's chorus, because this is the one I observed first

II. **Second Main Point Men's** Chorus is unlike any course I've ever taken
Listener Relevance Link: Everyone has taken a class outside of their major in which nobody talks to ach other and the idea seems to be to spend as little time in the room as possible

A. **Subpoint:** The men's chorus is not like that; the atmosphere is totally different.

1. **Sub-Subpoint:** Everyone seems to be friends; they all get to class early and stay late seemingly just to socialize. Neal Donhoff: "It's definitely the most unique class I've taken. It's more relaxed than getting a lecture, and it's pretty fun a lot of the time too"

2. **Sub-Subpoint:** The 1 hour credit class seems to function more like a club, where everyone is friends. This may have something to do with the history of university choirs and glee clubs, which are traditionally extra-curricular activities not classes according to Leonard van Camp's 1965 essay, The Formation of A Cappella Choirs

B. **Subpoint:** The diversity present made this cohesiveness even more impressive.

1. **Sub-Subpoint:** The age range in the choir fluctuated between freshmen and graduate students, and there was probably 25 or 30 African Americans among the 70 members.

2. **Sub-Subpoint:** Neal Donhoff also commented on the fact that many different majors choir members come from, as well as the fact that several members are homosexual.

Transition: I then visited the men's chorus's larger counterpart, the 100-member women's choir

III. **Third Main Point** The women's choir, while seemingly less diverse, offered me an opportunity to study a women's gorup

Listener Relevance Link: Many guys have never been around any all women's organization, let alone one in such a unique setting.

    A. **Subpoint:** The women's choir is sort of like the men's but in some ways isn't

        1. **Sub-Subpoint:** Like the men's choir, the women show up early to socialize in groups, as many seem to be friends.

        2. **Sub-Subpoint:** However, the diversity doesn't seem to be as pronounces, as about 1/3 of the men's choir is African American, only about 10% of the women's choir is. The diversity of the group comes from drawing a larger percentage of people from across campus

    B. **Subpoint:** There also seems to be some amount of drama in the group not present in the men's choir.

        1. **Sub-Subpoint:** There was drama, less evident in the practice, more evident when I observed the choirs backstage at their Christmas concert. The lower singing parts (the altos) were not fond of the higher singing parts (sopranos)

        2. **Sub-Subpoint:** This was more evident in the smaller A Cappella group called Paws and Listen, probably because this group is student run and not run by a professor.

Transition: Through this observation, I learned a lot about intercultural communities.

CONCLUSION

    I. **Restatement of Thesis:** The choirs, which function more as clubs, have an impressive cohesiveness despite their diverse and unique composition.

    II. **Summary of Main Points:** Contrary to what I expected going in, the men's and women's choirs are fun and interesting groups.

    III. **Clincher:** I feel that I'm better off now having been on the other side of cultural groups that I am not a part of.

REFERENCES

Format them according to APA style (as directed by your instructor).

FORMAL OUTLINE

NAME: Amanda Kirby

TITLE: Meade County; Can't Get Much Smaller Than This

INTRODUCTION

   I. **Attention Catcher:** (Question) What do you think of when you think about the country? (Show Picture) Did you think of this?

   II. **Listener Relevance Link:** Some of you may not know about the country life but it is pretty interesting and you should visit one day.

   III. **Speaker Credibility:** I have spent multiple days in Meade County, Brandenburg and I quickly learned all about living in the country.

   IV. **Thesis Statement:** While visiting Meade County, it was nothing of what I expected. I learned how different it was and it changed the way I look at country lifestyles.

   V. **Preview:** Today I am going to talk about how I perceived the country life as being, what I experienced while I was there, and how I feel about it now.

BODY

   I. **First Main Point:** Since I live in Louisville my whole life, which is a larger city, I did not have a sure idea how to perceive a small town.

Listener Relevance Link: Over 75% of you live or have lived in a large city before and know what it's like.

   A. **Subpoint:** (Country Landscape Picture) When I found out I was going to be entering a small country town, I was expecting to see red barns, open land, people with no shoes or teeth, and lots of livestock.

     1. **Sub-Subpoint:** Referring back to the first picture in my slide. (Show Picture again) This is what I thought everyone would look like.

     2. **Sub-Subpoint:** I thought there wasn't going to be anything to do there. I thought it was going to be boring, quiet and a place where you just sat around.

Transition: [Even though some of these things may be true, there is way more to this small town than I thought. Now I am going to talk about what I did and experienced while I was there]

   II. **Second Main Point:** In the few days of being here, I quickly learned that there was more to do than I ever imagined.

Listeners Relevance Link: I am sure that everyone here has gone into a situation blind, not knowing what was going to occur.

    A. **Subpoint:** The environment is so peaceful and everyone is always so friendly.

        1. **Sub-Subpoint:** No matter what, everyone says hi to everyone and pets are openly allowed in stores. (Story about friends parents dog)

        2. **Sub-Subpoint:** Since most everyone has at least three acres to themselves, it's hard to hear your neighbors or anyone else for that matter. It's very serene.

    A. **Subpoint:** There are many more activities to do than I thought.

        1. **Sub-Subpoint:** Some of the interesting things to do is possibly ride your go-cart or jump on a trampoline or play hide and seek. Since there is so much extra room, you can basically do whatever you want.

        2. **Sub-Subpoint:** Some things that are unique to Meade County are the Meade County Fair (Show truck picture), Otter Creek, Doe Valley golf, etc.

Transition: [In knowing what the country life is really like, this is how I will always remember my experience.]

    III. **Third Main Point:** What I have experienced has changed me in more ways than one.
Listeners Relevance Link: Everyone in here has had a life changing event occur to them.

    A. **Subpoint:** It really made me consider living in a place like this.

        1. **Sub-Subpoint:** Knowing how peaceful it is, and that there are actually things to do, it has really made me take into consideration if I should live there when I get older or not. I feel like it has more to offer than a larger city and it fits my lifestyle more. (Show picture of house)

Transition: [Since this event, I have learned not to judge a book by its cover.]

CONCLUSION

    I. **Restatement of Thesis:** Since I have visited, Meade County, it was nothing of what I expected. I learned how different it was and it changed the way I look at country lifestyles.

    II **Summary of Main Points:** After talking about how I perceived the country life as being much different than a city lifestyle and experiencing what I did while I was there, has made me change the way I perceived it.

    III. **Clincher:** Going into an environment that is completely different from what you are used it isn't always a bad thing, and if you ever get the chance, you should travel to a little less populated town and see how it really is.

FORMAL OUTLINE

Kyle Wooley

INTRODUCTION:

I. **Attention Catcher:** What would you consider a normal daily routine? Is it waking up just in time to brush your teeth, comb your hair, get dressed and scurry off to school? Or is it waking up before sunrise to pray the first of five prayers for the day?

II. **Listener Relevance link:** Informing others of a community and the observations I obtained.

III. **Speaker Credibility:** I took place in fieldwork and observations, gathered primary research.

IV. **Thesis Statement:** I will talk about my experience with exploring a different community. I will share how the Muslim community carries out a normal day. Lastly, I will focus on the interesting facts I found and the reaction I had with them.

V. **Preview:** I have gained a greater respect and acceptance for other communities. I also learned a lot of behaviors that I will practice during my everyday life.

BODY:

I. **First Main Point:** Growing up with a strong Christian background, I have a great amount of prior knowledge in Religion.

    a. **Subpoint:** My first instinct is to compare the two religions, but I later realize that I should be open and learn as much as I can instead of pointing out differences.

    b. **Subpoint 2:** During my experience with the Muslim Community I found a lot of similarities within the two religions and gained a greater appreciation for my own religion, and giving more effort.

Transition: Some examples of the obedience shown by the Muslim community are the extensive rituals they practice.

I. **Second Main Point:** So, I am going to focus on the Rituals that seemed unusual based on my culture. Also I will talk about the buildings that are used within this community.

    a. **Subpoint:** The Muslim community takes part in Five prayers a day (Salat). One before sunrise, noon, afternoon, evening, sunset.

    b. **Subpoint2:** Rituals taken place before prayer can be done: Wa'du Station. Washing of the body must take place before prayer can be carried out.

c. **Subpoint 3:** The building that holds the mosque for the Muslim community in Lexington is the Lexington Islamic Center. The place is a run down home across from memorial hall that has been converted to a worship center. Use example of the experience with Christian church members not attending a church unless it is nice and up-to-date with technology.

Transition: After observing this very dedicated community I have received a lot of life long lessons.

III. **Conclusion:**

a. **Restatement of Thesis:** I shared with you today the way exploring deeper in this community has given me a different look within my own religion. I have gained a greater appreciation and obedience in my spiritual life. I have obtained a better understanding and acceptance of other cultures and communities. I couldn't have picked a better culture to become a part of. Not only did this experience help me with my ability to become a part of and effectively analyze another culture, I was able to completely change my behavior in many parts of my life.

b. **Summary of Main Points:** Growing up with a strong Christian background was an advantage and disadvantage at the same time. I was able to understand some of the reasons for their rituals, while I found myself comparing my religion to some of the other rituals. Secondly, I talked about how it doesn't matter what we do when we are becoming a spiritual, religious person. Just as long as we are becoming better people in the process.

c. **Clincher:** The definition of religion is: the belief in and worship of a god or gods. So whether we are washing ourselves before we pray, or singing worship songs on Sunday mornings. We are all in it for the same reason.

Composition and Communication II: Analyzing Arguments &Persuading and Working with Others

GROUP COMMUNICATION

Communicating in Groups

Team-building

Perspective-taking

Group Contract

Group Reflection

WORKING IN A GROUP: MY EXPERIENCE

Goal: Students will discuss their experiences working with groups and create a list of those experiences with options on how to maintain the positive and resolve the negative.

Rationale: To help students see the positives and negatives of working in a group, and how to maintain or change those experiences for a successful group experience.

Directions: List positive and negative experiences you have had with working with others in a group. How did you feel when the experience was positive? Negative? What could be repeated to have a successful interaction? What could have been done differently?

POSITIVE EXPERIENCES	NEGATIVE EXPERIENCES

Created by: Renee Kaufmann, University of Kentucky

GROUP ROLE INVENTORY

Goal: To become aware of the roles you play in your group and of how others perceive your roles.

Rationale: When you see yourself differently from the way others see you, when there is a difference between role perception and role enactment, and when your expectations of people cloud your perceptions of them, there is a potential source of uncertainty, confusion, frustration, and conflict. The Group Role Inventory was designed to help members become more aware of the roles they play and of how others perceive those roles. It is time-consuming—it takes at least forty-five minutes—but often worth the time and effort it takes, particularly when a group is having trouble establishing norms. The Group Role Inventory can also be an effective means for dealing with one or two problem members by bringing everyone's role expectations into the discussion rather than by ganging up on the so-called troublemakers.

Directions:

1. Fill out Group Role Inventory Sheet

2. Go over the list and check the role you would like to have performed but did not perform.

3. Go over the list again and star (*) the role you performed but would rather not have performed.

4. Discuss results with your group.

Materials: Group Role Inventory Sheet (attached)
Time: Forty-five minutes
Participants: Ongoing groups

Application: The exercise should make members aware of how roles are used in their groups.

Taken from: Beebe, S.A., & Masterson, J.T. (1997). *Communicating in small groups: Principles and practices* (5th ed.). New York: Addison Wesley Longman, Inc. (99-100).

GROUP ROLE INVENTORY SHEET

Who in your group, including yourself, is most likely to:

1. Take initiative, propose ideas, get things started?

2. Sit back and wait passively for others to lead?

3. Express feelings most freely, frankly, openly?

4. Keep feelings hidden, reserved, unexpressed?

5. Show understanding of other members' feelings?

6. Be wrapped up in personal concerns and not very responsive to others?

7. Interrupt others when they are speaking?

8. Daydream, be lost in private thoughts during group sessions, be "far away"?

9. Give you a feeling of encouragement, warmth, friendly interest, support?

10. Converse privately with someone else while another member is speaking to the group?

11. Talk of trivial things, engage in superficial chitchat?

12. Criticize, put people on their guard?

13. Feel superior to other members?

14. Be listened to by everyone while speaking?

15. Feel inferior to other members?

16. Contribute good ideas?

17. Contradict, disagree, argue, raise objections?

18. Sulk or withdraw when the group is displeasing?

19. Be the one you would like to have on your side if a conflict arose in the group?

20. Agree or conform with whatever is said?

21. Be missed, if absent, more than any other member?

Taken from: Beebe, S.A., & Masterson, J.T. (1997). *Communicating in small groups:* Principles and practices (5th ed.). New York: Addison Wesley Longman, Inc. (99-100).

STARTING LINE-UP: GROUP PRESENTATIONS OF INTRODUCTION

Goal: Students will demonstrate Tuckman's Team Development Model (steps: Forming, Storming, Norming, Performing) through their group presentation. Students will reflect on what it means to be a group member, along with their experiences during the process of forming, storming, and norming the group.

Rationale: To help students ease public speech anxiety and to aid in the forming, storming, norming, performing part of Tuckman's Model.

Directions:
Forming: We are going to number off and you will get into your new group. Discuss the following once everyone is seated.

1. Introduce yourself:
- Name
- Major
- Explain why you choose UK
- Teams need to identify their purpose, develop group norms, identify group processes, define roles, build relationships and trust (to transition to Storming)

Storming: You and your group will need to venture out and **do something as a group** (for example, participate in a sports activity together, go to a coffee shop to chat, or think of something everyone have in common—and go do it!) This needs to be documented with a photo of the group and will need to be explained in your Starting Line-Up presentations. *The purpose of this activity is to get your group to the next step... norming.* What you and your group need to do is: pick a place, date, and time to meet. Once that is established, discuss possible ideas for your group's identity.
The group must present its:
- Group Name
- Group Logo
- Group Motto

Norming and Performing: You and your group will do a 5-6 presentation. You will need to have a visual aid with your team name, logo, and motto. As a group, must have 2 visuals (one of the logo and one of your group together at your outside activity). Your group must tell about your group experience and how you all felt you achieve "group cohesion" up to this point.

Created by: Randi Campbell and Renee Kaufmann, University of Kentucky

SPACE SURVIVAL: TEAM BUILDING EXERCISE

Goal: To practice group communications skills and continue building group cohesion.

Rationale: This activity will help students see the importance of listening and responding in a group.

Directions: In the following situation, your "life" and "death" will depend upon how well your team can share its present knowledge of a relatively unfamiliar situation so that the team can make decisions that will lead to your survival. This problem is fictional, although the ranking to which you will compare your results was done by a number of space experts.

Read the situation and do Step 1 without discussing it with your other team members.

THE SITUATION

You are a member of a lunar exploration crew originally scheduled to rendezvous with a mother ship on the lighted surface of the moon. Due to mechanical difficulties however, your ship was forced to land at a spot some 320 kilometers (200 miles) from the rendezvous point. During the re-entry and landing, much of the equipment aboard was damaged, and, since survival depends on reaching the mother ship, the most critical items available must be chosen for the 320 km trip.

YOUR TASK

On the next page are listed the 15 items left intact and undamaged after landing. Your task is to rank these items according to their importance in aiding you to reach the mother ship, starting with "1" the more important, to "15" the least important. You should assume the number in the crew is the same as the number on your team, you are the actual people in the situation, the team has agreed to stick together, and all 15 items are in good condition.

Exercise adapted from: Hall, J. (1971). Decisions, decisions. *Psychology Today*, 51-56.

Step 1: Each person is to individually rank each item. 1 is most important; 15 is least important. Do not discuss the situation or the task until each member has finished the individual ranking.

Step 2: Rank order the 15 items as a team. Once discussion begins, do not change your individual ranking.

ITEM	STEP 1 INDIVIDUAL RANKING	STEP 2 TEAM RANKING	STEP 3 EXPERT RANKING	STEP 4 DIFFERENCE RANKING |1-3|	STEP 5 DIFFERENCE RANKING |2-3|
Box of matches					
Food concentrate					
20 meters of nylon rope					
Parachute silk					
Portable heating unit					
Two .45 caliber pistols					
One case dehydrated milk					
Two 50 kg tanks of oxygen					
Stellar map (of the moon's Constellations)					
Life raft					
Magnetic compass					
25 liters of water					
Signal flares					
First aid kit w/ hypodermic needle					
Solar-power FM receiver/transmitter					
Total the absolute differences of Steps 4 and 5: (The lower the score the better.)				Your Score	Team Score

Exercise adapted from: Hall, J. (1971). Decisions, decisions. *Psychology Today*, 51-56.

PERSPECTIVE-TAKING AND GROUP CONFLICT

Goal: To help students see how their peers view the same community and how they would approach solving a problem.

Rationale: Students will see other's perspectives (and interests) of problems and solutions to these problems within the community.

Directions: Your group has been given $1,000 to use to improve an aspect of life in Lexington. You must all agree on how to use the money….and you must agree quickly. You have 25 minutes to design your plan. You also need to create one PowerPoint slide that your group will use when you present your plan to the class.

First, answer the following questions as an INDIVIDUAL.

1. What are 3 of the biggest problems in Lexington?

2. Which problem do you think you could make the biggest difference with using just $1,000?

3. How many people will your solution need to make it happen?

4. How long will it take to make your solution a reality?

5. What possible barriers could there be to your idea?

Now, your group should discuss the answers to your questions above and come to a consensus on how to spend your money.

1. What is the problem your group will address?

2. What is the solution?

3. What are potential challenges to making your plan a reality?

4. Construct a game plan – people, timeline, etc.

5. Design your PowerPoint slide. Create a sketch below.

Finally, answer the following questions about the *group process* to reach the decision.

1. Was there debate about what the best problem and/or solution would be for your project? How was it resolved?

2. Did everyone have a chance to voice his or her opinion about what the best idea was?

3. Thinking back to C&C 1, what conflict management styles did members of your group use (withdrawing, competing, accommodating, compromising, collaborating)?

Created by: Sarah Kercsmar, University of Kentucky

LEADERSHIP QUESTIONNAIRE

Directions: The following items describe aspects of leadership behavior. Respond to each item according to the way you would most likely act if you were the leader of a work group. Check whether you would most likely behave in the described way: always (A), frequently (F), occasionally (O), seldom (S), or never (N).

	A	F	O	S	N
1. I would most likely act as the spokesman of the group.					
2. I would encourage overtime work.					
3. I would allow members complete freedom in their work.					
4. I would encourage the use of uniform procedures.					
5. I would permit the members to use their own judgment in solving problems.					
6. I would stress being ahead of competing groups.					
7. I would speak as a representative of the group.					
8. I would needle members for greater effort.					
9. I would try out my ideas in the group.					
10. I would let the members do their work the way they think best.					
11. I would be working hard for a promotion.					
12. I would tolerate postponement and uncertainty.					
13. I would speak for the group if there were visitors present.					
14. I would keep the work moving at a rapid pace.					
15. I would turn the members loose on a job and let them go to it.					
16. I would settle conflicts when they occur in the group.					
17. I would get swamped by details.					
18. I would represent the group at outside meetings.					
19. I would be reluctant to allow the members any freedom of action.					
20. I would decide what should be done and how it should be done.					
21. I would push for increased production.					
22. I would let some members have authority, which I could keep.					
23. Things would usually turn out as I predicted.					
24. I would allow the group a high degree of initiative.					
25. I would assign group members to particular tasks.					
26. I would be willing to make changes.					
27. I would ask the group members to work harder.					
28. I would trust the group members to exercise good judgment.					
29. I would schedule the work to be done.					
30. I would refuse to explain my actions.					

31. I would persuade others that my ideas are to their advantage.
32. I would permit the group to set its own pace.
33. I would urge the group to beat its previous record.
34. I would act without consulting the group.
35. I would ask that group members follow standard rules and regulations.

A	F	O	S	N

SCORING PROCEDURES FOR LEADERSHIP GRID

1. Circle the item number for questionnaire items: 1, 4, 7, 13, 16, 17, 18, 19, 20, 23, 29, 30, 31, 34 and 35.
2. Write a 1 in front of the circled items to which you responded S (seldom) or N (never).
3. Write a 1 in front of items not circled to which you responded A (always) or F (frequently).
4. Circle the 1's which you have written in front of the following items: 3, 5, 8, 10, 12, 15, 17, 19, 22, 24, 26, 28, 30, 32 and 34.
5. Count the circled 1's. This is your person orientation (P) score. Record the score in the blank following the letter P below.
6. Count the uncircled 1's. This is your task orientation (T) score. Record this number in the blank following the letter T.

T: _____ P:_____

In order to locate your position on the Leadership Grid below (see grid on page 150), find your score on the Person dimension (P), the horizontal axis of the graph. Next, move up the column corresponding to your P score to the cell that corresponds to your Task or T score. Place an X in the cell that represents your two scores. Numbers in parentheses correspond to the major management style in Black and McCanse's (1991) Leadership Grid (formerly the Managerial Grid developed by Black and Mouton (1985)).

The T-P Leadership Questionnaire is reprinted from *A Handbook of Structured Experiences for Human Relations Training*, Vol. 1, rev., edited by J. William Pfeiffer and John E. Jones. La Jolla, CA: University Associates, 1974.

15
14
13
12
11
10
9
8
7
6
5
4
3
2
1

(1,9)		(9,9)
	(5,5)	
(1,1)		(9,1)

1 2 3 4 5 6 7 8 9 10 11 12 13 14 15 16 17 18 19 20

GROUP EXPECTATIONS

Goal: To create accountability and ownership for each member's actions within the group.

Rationale: Creating a group contract will build cohesiveness, norms, and expectations for the group.

Directions: Read the process and firing a member steps below. Think about how this will apply to your group's construction of the group contract. Read the following group contact forms and as a group decide what will work best to suit your group.

THE PROCESS

1. The group must develop a "Contract" stating expectations and responsibilities for membership.

2. Members must date and document efforts of other members *each day that the group meets.*

3. Groups are required to meet *in the classroom* on each assigned "group work day." The instructor *will be present for* the first 15 minutes of those sessions.

4. Groups are required to meet a *minimum* of one time *out of classroom.* The instructor will not be present for this meeting.

5. If a group determines that a particular member is not meeting his or her contractual responsibilities, the "firing" process can be initiated.

"FIRING" A MEMBER

1. Once a group has determined that one member is not meeting his or her contractual responsibilities, the group meets with that member (*while the instructor is present*) to discuss concerns and agree upon one more chance to live up to expectations. The group, the individual member, and the instructor review and discuss documentation of failed expectations.

2. If the member fails to meet expectations again after the initial meeting (#1), the group has grounds to "fire" him or her.

3. "Firing" must occur *before* the in-class rehearsal day.

4. A "fired" member must then create and deliver an individual actuation persuasive speech for a maximum of 35 points. (Loss "group participation" points).

5. All students must turn in "group summative peer critique form" on their scheduled speaking day.

6. Grievance Procedure: Dissatisfied students may elect to follow the grievance procedure as stated on the syllabus.

Adapted from "Com 181: Public Speaking Workbook" Deanna Sellnow

GROUP CONTRACT

We, _____

_____ (your names) agree to work together as a group on the next speech project. As a group we will abide by the following terms:

1. **Commitment to group goal:** (What is the goal of the group? How will you determine if someone is not committed to this goal?)

2. **On-track Discussion:** (What steps will be taken to keep the meetings focused and effective? What are the consequences for group members who do not adhere to these steps?)

3. **Fulfilling individual assignments:** (How will individual assignments be delegated? What are the consequences for group members who do not have their work done on time? What protocol should be followed if a member cannot attend a group meeting?)

4. **Interpersonal conflict:** (How will the group deal with conflict?)

5. **Including all members:** (What are the expectations for group participation? What format will be used to encourage member participation?)

6. **Firing Process**

Signatures:

Taken from "Com 181: Public Speaking Workbook" Deanna Sellnow

SAMPLE GROUP CONTRACT

We, _____, _____, _____, and _____ have all agreed upon the following document as a contract that will govern the members of our group. The hope is that this document will help us stay on task, meet all scheduled deadlines, and present our topic respectively. It is our aspiration to achieve no fewer than 90% of all possible points in our presentation.

The foundations for our group's firing process is a series of warnings from the other group members. Each group member is allotted three warnings. Upon receiving the third warning that member will be removed from the group. The amount of warnings given out for a single infraction will vary based on the seriousness of the violation. All warnings must be a written description of what contract infringement took place and every group member, except for the person receiving the warning, must sign it.

Our group will attempt to stay focused and effective throughout our meetings. To attain this each member will be asked to take on a substantial amount of responsibility.

At the beginning of each meeting we will draft a list of our objectives. All group members are expected to be present and on time to all in-class and out-of-class meetings. All group members will be expected to give their utmost effort and participation. All work will be divided evenly among the group as not to overload one particular person. If someone believes they are being treated unfairly it is their job to bring it to the attention of the rest of the group. If there is a conflict between members the majority will always win. If a tie between members occurs [INSERT INSTRUCTOR'S NAME] will have the deciding vote.

Being absent from class or group meetings will only be excused if there are extenuating circumstances, *i.e., death in the family, or car troubles.* It will be at the discretion of the group whether an excuse is acceptable. If someone knows in advance that they will not be able to attend class or a group meeting it is their duty to notify a minimum of two group members.

Guidelines for Warnings are as Follows:

Nonparticipation: 1 Warning

Not completing tasks: 1 Warning

10-15 minutes late: 1 Warning

15-30 minutes late: 2 Warnings

30+ minutes late: 3 Warnings

Signatures

Group Member

_____   ___/___/_____

Group Member

_____   ___/___/_____

Group Member

_____   ___/___/_____

Group Member

_____   ___/___/_____

Group Member

_____   ___/___/_____

Taken from "Com 181: Public Speaking Workbook" Deanna Sellnow

GROUP MEETING REFLECTION FORM

Meeting Date: _____

Your Name: _____

Goal: To create accountability and ownership for each member's actions within the group outside of class.

Rationale: Having students reflect on their contributions as well as others' contributions during the group work process will encourage communication and help foster cohesiveness.

Directions: After each group meeting, provide ethical critiques for both your group members and yourself. Rate each individual on his/her performance in the group. Justify the rating with specific examples taken from the guidelines of ethical group behavior:

- committed to the goals of the group
- fulfills individual assignments
- avoids interpersonal conflicts
- encourages group participation
- helps keep the discussion on track

Each critique should use "I" language and should be balanced, discussing strengths as well as weaknesses of each group member.

Yourself _____

Circle Overall Individual Rating
   1   2   3   4   5   6   7
(Poor)   (Met requirements)   (Excellent)

Tasks accomplished:

Tasks assigned:

Ethical critique:

Group Member _____

Circle Overall Individual Rating
   1   2   3   4   5   6   7
(Poor)   (Met requirements)   (Excellent)

Tasks accomplished:

Tasks assigned:

Ethical critique:

Group Member _____

Circle Overall Individual Rating

    1   2   3   4   5   6   7

(Poor) (Met requirements)   (Excellent)

Tasks accomplished:

Tasks assigned:

Ethical critique:

Group Member _____

Circle Overall Individual Rating

    1   2   3   4   5   6   7

(Poor) (Met requirements)   (Excellent)

Tasks accomplished:

Tasks assigned:

Ethical critique:

Group Member _____

Circle Overall Individual Rating

    1   2   3   4   5   6   7

(Poor) (Met requirements)   (Excellent)

Tasks accomplished:

Tasks assigned:

Ethical critique:

Adapted from "Com 181: Public Speaking Workbook" Deanna Sellnow

RHETORICAL ANALYSIS

Taking a Position

Annotated Bibliography

Rhetorical Analysis

Argument

Ethos, Pathos, and Logos

Enthymemes and Syllogisms

Fallacies

POSITION STATEMENT PREPARATION SHEET

Goal: To prepare you to write your position statement paper by brainstorming potential topics of interest.

Rationale: Having students view projects as small steps to accomplish rather than a large obstacle to tackle makes completing projects more manageable and generates less anxiety.

Directions: Using your free write from class and your notes from our class discussion, begin thinking about what topic might be appropriate your position statement.

1. List ten possible topics for your position statement.

2. Which 3 topics interest you most and why?

3. For each of your 3 potential topics, find at least three sources you would use to inform your paper.

    a.

    b.

    c.

4. Considering the availability of reliable sources and your level of interest/passion about the three topics you have selected, which topic will you use to write your position paper? (Remember, the next project involves finding a *visual artifact* related to your controversy to analyze. This could be a magazine article, commercial, website etc. Would your group have a hard time locating interesting visual artifacts to analyze?)

5. Using your current topic (If you haven't yet made a decision, just choose one of your three), propose a thesis statement and provide a rough idea of what your three supporting body paragraphs might be. (Remember! This is a *position* statement, not a research paper. What is informed position or stance are you taking on your topic. Your thesis will probably answer the former question. Your body paragraphs will most likely address the informed reasons why you took that position on that topic.)

Created by: Randi Campbell, University of Kentucky

ANNOTATED BIBLIOGRAPHY WORKSHEET

Goal: To help you prepare your position paper and annotated bibliography.

Rationale: By splitting up this assignment into smaller pieces it becomes more manageable and questions can be addressed before it is too late.

1. Briefly articulate the controversy you are writing your position paper on and your stance on that controversy.

2. Write the APA reference for your source below and answer the following questions about that information you gained from that source.

   a. APA Citation:

   b. Summarize the main points of the source.

   c. Evaluate the credibility of the source and claims.

   d. Describe how you will use it in your position paper or why you won't use it in your position paper.

3. Write the APA reference for your source below and answer the following questions about that information you gained from that source.

    a. APA Citation:

    b. Summarize the main points of the source.

    c. Evaluate the credibility of the source and claims.

    d. Describe how you will use it in your position paper or why you won't use it in your position paper.

4. Write the APA reference for your source below and answer the following questions about that information you gained from that source.

    a. APA Citation:

    b. Summarize the main points of the source.

    c. Evaluate the credibility of the source and claims.

    d. Describe how you will use it in your position paper or why you won't use it in your position paper.

Created by: Randi Campbell, University of Kentucky

THE RHETORICAL SITUATION

Goal: To help students visualize how the rhetorical situation works using a current example.

Rationale: Having students watch a clip and then apply the rhetorical situation as a class will foster conversation about each element and serve as a tool for application.

Directions: Watch the following clip and fill-in the rhetorical situation below. Make sure to provide examples or support.

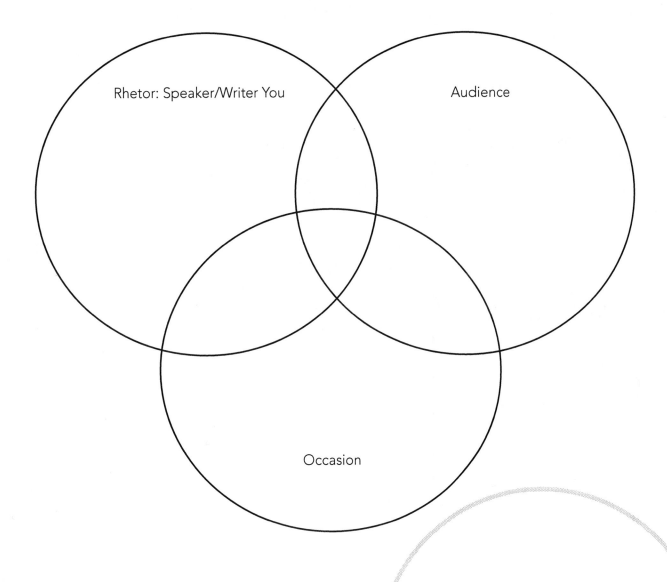

Created by: Renee Kaufmann, University of Kentucky

RHETORICAL ANALYSIS: NEO-ARISTOTELIAN METHOD

Goal: To help ease anxiety about the Neo-Aristotelian Method.

Rationale: The best way to learn how to do rhetorical analysis … is to just do it! Thinking about the argument in front of you, provide as much information as you can about each category. It's better to have "too much" information as you sit down to write your formal paper than not enough. We are using a style of rhetorical criticism called **Neo-Aristotelian** criticism.

Remember, in rhetorical criticism, it is not enough to just say WHAT is being done, but you also have to explain WHY.

Directions: Read the transcript provided and the watch the speech. Fill out the boxes below with your analysis.

CANON	DESCRIBE WHAT	EXPLAIN WHY
Invention (content)		
Arrangement (organization)		
Style (language)		

CANON	DESCRIBE WHAT	EXPLAIN WHY
Delivery (body and voice)		
Memory (memorable)		

1. Was this an effective message? Why or why not?

2. What was the rhetor's exigency?

Created by: Sarah Kercsmar, University of Kentucky

RHETORICAL FIGURES IN VISUAL ARGUMENTS

Goal: To have students recognize how rhetorical figure are used within in visuals.

Rationale: Having students examine the rhetorical devices will make them congnizant of the different stragies used in visual arguments.

Directions: Label each photo according to the rhetorical figure it illustrates.

1. _____

2. _____

3. _____

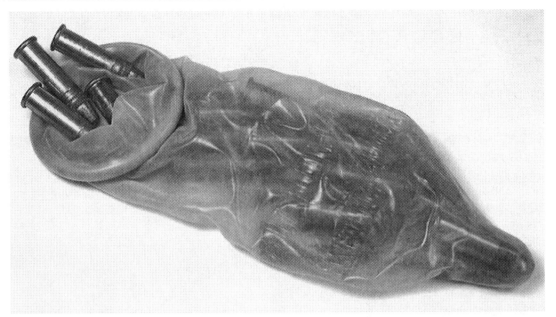

4. _____

Created by: Anna Rankin, University of Kentucky

NEO-ARISTOTELIAN ANALYSIS
IS THIS MESSAGE EFFECTIVE?

Goal: To help students check their papers to ensure all parts of a Neo-Aristotelian analysis were examined.

Rationale: Practicing the use of neo-Aristotelian perspective in class will provide students with the opportunity to question and engage with an artifact.

Directions: Read the questions below along with your Neo-Aristotelian analysis. Ask yourself, did I answer these questions in my paper?

DESCRIBE

1. **Rhetorical Situation**

    a. Speaker (rhetor)

        i. Who created the argument/message? What do we know about this person/organization/company?

        ii. Through what medium/channel is the argument being sent?

    b. Audience

        i. Who is the target audience? Why? How do you know?

    c. Topic

        i. What is the argument about?

        ii. Is it an argument of fact, definition, evaluation/causality, or proposal?

    d. Purpose

        i   Why is this artifact being shared?

        ii. Is it an argument to: inform, convince, persuade, explore, make decisions, meditate or pray, academic argument, invitational argument, rogerian argument?

    e. Occasion

        i. When is this artifact being shared?

        ii. Is it an argument of past, present, future (or a combination)?

   f. Exigence

       i. What is the *need* the rhetor is trying to fulfill?

   g. Constraints

       i. What are some things that may constrain possible decisions or actions the rhetor is trying to achieve?

INTERPRET

1. Invention (Content)

   a. Is their content well developed?

   b. Do they present a focused argument with "new" knowledge or insight?

   c. Inartistic proofs

       i. Uses Primary Research?

          1. Interviews, Fieldwork observations, Surveys and questionnaires, Experiments, Personal experience

       ii. Uses Secondary Research?

          1. Library sources, Online sources

       iii. Types of Supporting Material

          1. Facts, Statistics, Definition, Description, Explanation, Example, Testimony, Compare/Contrast, Narrative, Anecdote

       iv. Does the Rhetor Use Good Sources?

          1. Authority, Objectivity, Relevance, Currency, Credibility?

       v. Does the Rhetor Use Evidence Effectively?

          1. Consider Audiences?

             a. Relevant, accurate, valid, reliable, timely, understandable, relatable, typical (not extreme)

          2. Building a Critical Mass

             a. Does the rhetor avoid circumstantial evidence?

d. Artistic Proofs

  i. Ethos

    1. Character and Competence

      a. Authority

      b. Integrity/Trustworthiness/Honesty/Credibility/Likeability

        i. Initial, derived, terminal credibility

      c. Motives/Empathy/Respect for an audience and its values

  ii. Pathos

    1. What emotions are being displayed?

    2. How does the artifact use emotions?

    3. Do the emotions help to build a bridge (connecting with readers to assure them the rhetor understands their experiences) or sustain an argument (making logical claims stronger or more memorable)?

    4. If humor is used, what are the implications?

  iii. Logos

    1. Hard evidence (inartistic appeals)

      a. Facts, surveys/polls, stats, testimonies, narratives

    2. Reason and common sense (artistic appeals)

      a. Inductive Reasoning

      b. Deductive reasoning

        ii. Syllogism

        iii. Enthymeme

      c. Cultural assumptions and values

      d. Are there any argument fallacies?

2. Arrangement (Macrostructure)

a. In what format is the argument/message presented?

    i. Toulmin argument

        1. Identify claim, evidence/reason, warrant, backing

    ii. Argument to convince

        1. Comparative advantage

        2. Criteria satisfaction

        3. Refutative arrangement

        4. Statement of reasons

    iii. Argument to incite action

        1. Problem-solution

        2. Problem-cause-solution

        3. Cause and effect? Before and after?

        4. Monroe's motivated sequence

            a. Attention, need, satisfaction, visualization, call to action

b. Is the evidence arranged effectively/placed in key places in the paper?

c. *If it's a primarily visual argument…*

    i. How do the visual images and text work well together?

    ii. What is your eye drawn to first? Why?

    iii. How is the argument aligned to move your eye?

    iv. What's in the foreground/background? Why?

3. Style (Language)

a. Did it increase clarity, develop vividness, arouse emotions, foster a sense of inclusion, aid in understanding, make argument memorable?

b. Does the style match the overall tone the argument is trying to convey?

    i. High, medium, low style?

c.   Do they use jargon, slang, and colloquial terms?

d.   Do they control connotation?

e.   Do they use language that is concrete and specific? Or is it abstract?

f.   How are their sentences structured?

g.   Do they use punctuation to enhance their argument?

h.   Do they use figurative language?

   i.   Tropes (metaphor, simile, analogy, signifying, hyperbole, understatement, rhetorical questions, antonomasia, pun, irony)

   ii.   Schemes (parallelism, antithesis, inverted word order, anaphora)

4. Delivery

a.   Speech

   i.   Use of body

      1. Eye contact, poise, attire, facial expression, gestures

   ii.   Use of voice

      1. Conversational, intelligent/fluent, emotional expression/enthusiasm, emphasis

b.   *If it's a primarily written/visual argument...*

   i.   How do light and/or color set the tone?

   ii.   Consider typography (overall balance and arrangement of letters on the page or screen)

      1. Font, size, and typeface

         a.   Is it easy to read?

         b.   Does it clarify structure?

         c.   Does it reinforce the emotional tone conveyed?

   iii.   What does the font imply about the message?

      1. Consider its tone and mood

   iv.   Does the visual follow traditional conventions of its genre or stretch the boundaries of traditional media?

1. Does it use the CRAP method effectively?

    a. Contrast, repetition, alignment, proximity?

    b. Are the visual images and verbal text congruent?

  v. How does the channel (video, text, image) influence the message?

  vi. How does the medium (TV, film, radio, Internet, newspaper, magazine) influence the message? How is it used to communicate words and images? How would the message be altered if different media were used?

  vii. Is this the most effective way to present/disseminate the data chosen?

5. Memory

  a. Does the rhetor display mastery/control over the information delivered?

    i. Does it fully articulate its exigence?

    ii. Does it use a variety of rhetorical appeals?

    iii. Does it round the cycle of learning?

    iv. Does it integrate multiple channels and modalities?

  b. Is the argument memorable? How? Why?

EVALUATE – So what?

1. What is the effect of this artifact?

  a. Overall, how do you think people see this?

  b. Was the author successful in achieving its purpose?

2. What are the implications of this artifact?

  a. If people believe this and pay attention to this artifact, what may occur?

    i. What may change?

Created by: Nick Iannarino, University of Kentucky

ARGUMENT: USING THE TOULMIN MODEL

Goal: For students to understand how to construct an argument using the Toulmin Model.

Rationale: Stephen Toulmin (*The Uses of Argument*) provided a model of argument structure that gives us a tool for both evaluating and making arguments. The main parts of Toulmin's model are the **claim** (or conclusion), the **grounds/evidence/data** (also called the stated reason), and the **warrant** (also called the unstated assumption in the case of enthymemes).

Directions: Examine the arguments below using the Toulmin Method.

1. Initial argument: After-school sports programs are bad for teenagers because they take away study time.
   a. Claim: After school sports programs are bad for teenagers
   b. Stated reason: they take away study time
   c. Unstated assumption: [*loss of study time is bad for teenagers*]

2. Initial argument: After school sports programs are good for teenagers because they teach responsibility, teamwork, and time management.
   a. Claim:
   b. Stated reason:
   c. Unstated assumption:

3. Initial argument: Aquatic turtles make good pets for children because they are gentle.
   a. Claim:
   b. Stated reason:
   c. Unstated assumption:

4. Initial argument Aquatic Turtle make bad pets because they can carry salmonella poisoning
   a. Claim:
   b. Stated reason:
   c. Unstated assumption:

5. Initial argument: Sid is a bad team captain because he is too bossy
   a. Claim:
   b. Stated reason:
   c. Unstated assumption:

6. Initial argument: Sid is a good team captain because he is decisive in moments of crisis.
   a. Claim:
   b. Stated reason:
   c. Unstated assumption:

7. Initial argument: Cocaine and Heroin should not be legalized because legalization would greatly increase the number of drug addicts.
   a. Claim:
   b. Stated reason:
   c. Unstated assumption:

8. Unstated assumption Initial argument: Cocaine and heroin should be legalized because legalization would eliminate the black market in drugs.
   a. Claim:
   b. Stated reason:
   c. Unstated assumption:

9. Initial argument: Karate class is good for children because it promotes self confidence.
   a. Claim:
   b. Stated reason:
   c. Unstated assumption:

10. Initial argument: Karate class is bad for children because it encourages violence.
    a. Claim:
    b. Stated reason:
    c. Unstated assumption:

11. Initial argument: Welfare benefits for unwed mothers should be eliminated because elimination would greatly reduce the nation's illegitimacy rate.
    a. Claim:
    b. Stated reason:
    c. Unstated assumption:

12. Initial argument: Welfare benefits for unwed mothers should be retained in order to prevent poverty and hunger
    a. Claim:
    b. Stated reason:
    c. Unstated assumption

Created by: Jeff VanCleave, University of Kentucky

WHAT IS THE APPEAL?

Goal: For students to properly identify the rhetorical appeal and its purpose used within an ad.

Rationale: Sometimes creators of advertisements, campaigns, presentations, etc., use ethos, pathos, and or logos to convey a message to their audience. Having students identify and discuss the use of rhetorical appeals will make them more cognizant of the persuasion techniques used around them.

Directions: The image below is from a print advertisement. Answer the following questions below while analyzing the photo.

IMAGE #1:

Who is the intended audience?

Support for your claim (how do you know this?):

What is the exigency?

What rhetorical devices does the rhetor use within the advertisement?

If ethos is used, describe how it is used.

If pathos is used, explain how emotion conveyed.

If logos is used, explain what logic is used.

Created by: Renee Kaufmann, University of Kentucky

WHAT IS THE APPEAL (AGAIN)?

Goal: For students to properly identify the rhetorical appeal and its purpose used within an ad.

Rationale: Sometimes creators of advertisements, campaigns, presentations, etc., use ethos, pathos, and or logos to convey a message to their audience. Having students identify and discuss the use of rhetorical appeals will make them more cognizant of the persuasion techniques used around them.

Directions: The image below is from a print advertisement. Answer the following questions below while analyzing the photo.

IMAGE #2:

Image from: http://adsoftheworld.com/forum/exhibition/prius_print_ad

Who is the intended audience?

Support for your claim (how do you know this?):

What is the exigency?

What rhetorical devices does the rhetor use within the advertisement?

If ethos is used, describe how it is used.

If pathos is used, explain how emotion is conveyed.

If logos is used, explain what logic is used.

Created by: Renee Kaufmann, University of Kentucky

ETHOS

Goal: For students to properly describe the rhetorical appeal ethos as well the benefits, if any, it brings for the following public figures.

Rationale: Having students identify and discuss the use of ethos will make them more cognizant of it use around them.

Directions: Consider the ethos of each of the following public figures. Then describe one or two public arguments, campaigns, or products that might benefit from their endorsements as well as several that would not.

Oprah Winfrey- TV celebrity

Margaret Cho- Comedian

Kate Winslet- Actress

Sarah Palin- Former governor of Alaska and Republican vice-presidential candidate

Dave Chappelle- Humorists and columnist

Bill O'Reilly- TV news commentator

Marge Simpson- wife and mother on the show *The Simpsons*

John Stewart- Host of the Daily Show on Comedy Central

Adapted from Everything's An Argument 5th edition (2010) Andrea A. Lunsford and John J. Ruszkiewicz

ENTHYMEMES & SYLLOGISMS

Goal: For students to create a syllogism that supports the enthymeme.

Rationale: Understanding the terms enthymeme and syllogism will help students create stronger arguments in their papers.

Directions: An enthymeme is often the conclusion of a syllogism that presents a logical argument. Read the enthymemes below and create a syllogism that supports the conclusion (enthymeme).

Example:

ENTHYMEME:

Parents should not spank their children because it has negative psychological consequences.

SYLLOGISM:

    A. *Abuse causes negative psychological consequences.*

    B. *Spanking is abuse.*

    C. *Spanking should be prohibited because it causes negative psychological consequences.*

ENTHYMEME:

Sex education should be taught in schools because it will prevent unwanted pregnancies.

SYLLOGISM:

    A.

    B.

    C.

ENTHYMEME:

People over the age of 75 should not be allowed to possess a driver's license because it causes more accidents that are preventable.

SYLLOGISM:

A.

B.

C.

ENTHYMEME:

Schools should require uniforms for students because they prevent behavioral problems.

SYLLOGISM:

A.

B.

C.

Created by: Anna Rankin, University of Kentucky

ARGUMENT 1: FULL OF FALLACIES

Goal: To recognize and correct fallacies within text.

Rationale: Having students recognize and correct fallacies in other's writing will hopefully lead them to spot fallacies in their own writing.

Directions: Read the following paragraph and identify the fallacies that are represented.

The feminist argument that pornography is harmful has no merit and should not be discussed in college courses. I read "Playboy" magazine, and I don't see how it could be harmful. Feminists might criticize me for looking at porn, but they shouldn't talk; they obviously look at it, too, or they couldn't criticize it. Many important people, including the Presidents, writers, and entertainers who have been interviewed by the magazine and the women who pose in it, apparently agree. Scientific studies so far have not proved that pornography is harmful, so it must not be harmful. Besides, to be harmful, pornography would either have to harm the men who read it or the women who pose in it, and since they both choose these activities, they must not be harmful. Feminists should take a lesson from my parents—they don't like loud music and won't have it in their house, but they don't go around saying it's harmful to everyone or trying to prevent others from listening to it. Ever since feminists began attacking our popular culture, the moral foundation of our society has been weakened; the divorce rate, for example, continues to rise. If feminists would just cease their hysterical opposition to sex, perhaps relationships in our society would improve. If feminists insist, instead, on banning porn, men will have no freedom and no pleasure left, and large numbers of women will be jobless and will have to work as prostitutes to support themselves. In light of these consequences, feminists shouldn't be surprised if their protests are met with violence. Truly, the feminist argument is baseless.

Next steps: Now choose 2 of these arguments and write them out as complete logical syllogisms, filling in the missing premises.

On the left are the fallacious arguments from the previous paragraph; the explanation of them is on the right.

The feminist argument that pornography is harmful has no merit and should not be discussed in college courses.	This is the overall conclusion. "Should not be discussed in college courses" = unrelated to the arguments that follow, so this is missing the point.
I read "Playboy" magazine, and I don't see how it could be harmful.	"I read it"=ad populum, "I don't see how"=appeal to ignorance; also, hasty generalization to "Playboy" (as opposed to other porn) and on arguer's own experience.
Feminists might criticize me for looking at porn, but they shouldn't talk; they obviously look at it, too, or they couldn't criticize it.	Tu quoque; equivocation on "look at" (reading something to critique it is different from reading it regularly for pleasure).
Many important people, including the Presidents, writers, and entertainers who have been interviewed by the magazine and the women who pose in it, apparently agree.	Ad populum and appeal to authority.
Scientific studies so far have not proved that pornography is harmful, so it must not be harmful.	Appeal to ignorance.
Besides, to be harmful, pornography would either have to harm the men who read it or the women who pose in it, and since they both choose these activities, they must not be harmful.	False dichotomy (women who don't pose could still be harmed); unsupported assumption that people cannot be harmed by activities they have chosen.
Feminists should take a lesson from my parents—they don't like loud music and won't have it in their houses, but they don't go around saying it's harmful to everyone or trying to prevent others from listening to it.	Weak analogy.
Ever since feminists began attacking our popular culture, the moral foundation of our society has been weakened; the divorce rate, for example, continues to rise.	Post hoc; divorce rate=red herring.
If feminists would just cease their hysterical opposition to sex, perhaps relationships in our society would improve.	"Opposition to sex"=straw man; "hysterical"=ad hominem.
If feminists insist, instead, on banning porn, men will have no freedom and no pleasure left, and large numbers of women will be jobless and will have to work as prostitutes to support themselves.	Appeal to pity; slippery slope; did anyone actually suggest a ban?
In light of these consequences, feminists shouldn't be surprised if their protests are met with violence. Truly, the feminist argument is baseless.	Ad baculum: A fallacy we didn't discuss, in which the arguer basically says, "If you don't agree with my conclusion, bad things will happen to you." And saying the feminist argument is baseless begs the question—this is not additional evidence, but the exact claim the writer is hoping to establish (with "baseless" in place of "has no merit").

How might we make a stronger argument for the claim that "the feminist argument that pornography is harmful has no merit"? Let's try to construct an argument that avoids the fallacies above. Please note that much of the "evidence" here will be made up to serve as a model—don't use this page as a source for any actual research on pornography! We'll see what a good argument could look like, even if the evidence needed to make that argument doesn't currently exist.

The feminist argument that pornography is harmful lacks adequate support. First, the feminist argument typically alleges that pornography increases men's willingness to rape women, or at least to think of them only as sex objects. But this argument ignores the fact that the print pornography industry alone earns more money each year than the entire "legitimate" bookselling industry. For that to be true, there must be many, many men and women who read pornography regularly. And yet crime statistics suggest that not many men rape women. Furthermore, most men today believe in women's equality, as a study by Dr. Knowitall and her research group, of the Institute on the Status of Women, demonstrates. Feminists acknowledge that scientific studies have failed to show that porn harms women. If there had been only a few such studies, or if we had reason to believe they were unreliable, we should conclude that nothing has yet been shown about whether porn harms women. But I think that when reliable studies have repeatedly failed to show a relationship, that fact constitutes some evidence that the relationship doesn't exist. So it seems unlikely that porn is harming women in the way the feminist argument alleges.

In the absence of positive evidence from studies, we have to rely on common sense. Can people distinguish between the sometimes-degrading scenarios they see in porn and real life? I believe they can. I think pornography is a lot like television and movies—it presents images that, while they certainly do have some impact on us, we all realize are nothing more than fiction. Young children may have difficulty distinguishing between fantasy and reality, but they are not often exposed to pornography. Men and women who look at porn should know better than to think that it gives a realistic picture of sexual relationships between men and women. If porn cannot be shown to harm women as a class by making them more vulnerable to sexual violence or causing men to think of them as inferior, how else might it be harmful? Feminists have often argued that the porn industry is harmful to the women who work within it—that many of them are abused and exploited. I agree with them that if an industry is mistreating people, it needs to be reformed, and they are doing a public service by pointing out such abuses. But what sort of reform are feminists proposing?

One suggestion I know about has been made by Catharine MacKinnon and Andrea Dworkin, who argue that there should be a civil rights statute that allows anyone who has been harmed by porn to seek civil damages from pornographers. My concern about this proposal is that although it will not legally be censorship, since the law would not empower the government to stop anyone from producing material based on the ideas it contains, the civil rights statute will have the same effect as censorship. Pornographers may be so afraid of facing lawsuits that many of them will stop producing porn—and a situation where people are afraid to put forward certain kinds of writing or pictures because they will face legal consequences seems to violate the spirit, if not the letter, of the first amendment. Porn, like books, may express certain ideas about men, women, and sex, and those ideas may have political ramifications—but just as controversial books are protected, porn should be. It may even do more good than harm by provoking thoughtful discussion and debate about men, women, and sexuality.

DISTRIBUTING MESSAGES

Crafting a Persuasive Message

Group Presentation Formats

Memory, Delivery, and Presentational Aids

Group Dynamics

CRAFTING A PERSUASIVE MESSAGE

Goal: To recognize what canons are used and why within a group created persuasive message.

Rationale: By incorporating the canons, students understand the importance of using them to craft a persuasive message.

Directions: You are an executive at an advertising agency and you are about to launch a new campaign about being eating healthy and/or getting enough physical activity. You want to create the advertising campaign by keeping the Neo-Aristotelian canons in mind.

CHOOSE AN AUDIENCE:

Parents of young children

Doctors and nurses at a small rural hospital

Senior citizens in Florida

CHOOSE A TOPIC:

Healthy eating

Walking as a form of physical activity

Losing weight by exercising and eating well

CANON	DESCRIBE WHAT	DESCRIBE WHY
Invention (content)		
Arrangement (organization)		

CANON	DESCRIBE WHAT	DESCRIBE WHY
Style (language)		
Delivery		
Memory (memorable?)		

Now, create a 2-minute "sales pitch" for your ad campaign. You will present the speech to the class as an "impromptu."

Created by: Sarah Kercsmar, University of Kentucky

WHAT'S THE BEST FORMAT FOR YOUR MESSAGE?
EXAMINING SYMPOSIUM SPEECH FORMATS

Goal: Students will chose the symposium speech format that best suits the group's needs and message.

Rational: Having students examine the different types of symposiums will foster a discussion about their speech and the overall message.

Direction: The following pages contain graphic organizers for each symposium speech type. As a group examine which style best suits your group and exigency.

CHOICES:

Monroe's Motivated Sequence

Problem, Cause, Solution

Problem and Solution

MONROE'S MOTIVATED SEQUENCE WORKSHEET

	SOURCES	MAIN IDEAS
Attention		
Need		
Satisfaction *National* *Local* *Personal*		

	SOURCES	MAIN IDEAS
Visualization		
Action		

**Do not forget you will need an introduction, transitions, and conclusion, too!*

Created by: Sarah Kercsmar, University of Kentucky

PROBLEM/CAUSE/ SOLUTION WORKSHEET

	SOURCES	MAIN POINTS
PROBLEM		
CAUSE(S)		
SOLUTIONS National Local Personal		

**Do not forget you will need an introduction, transitions, and conclusions, too!*

Created by: Sarah Kercsmar, University of Kentucky

PROBLEM/SOLUTION WORKSHEET

	SOURCES	MAIN POINTS
PROBLEM		
SOLUTIONS *National* *Local* *Personal*		

**Do not forget you will need an introduction, transition, and conclusions, too!

Created by: Sarah Kercsmar, University of Kentucky

GROUP DELIVERY EXERCISE: IMPROMPTU INFOMERCIAL

Goal: To check students understanding of Monroe's Motivated Sequence.

Rationale: This speech will provide the opportunity for students to show their understanding of Monroe's Motivated Sequence.

Directions: After watching an infomercial and discussing how each part of Monroe's Motivated Sequence, with your group construct a 2-3 minute impromptu infomercial. Using an object in the classroom, create a speech that is designed for your audience. Please note each member will need a part in the speech and your group's goal is to get your audience to act (e.g. buy your product). Good Luck!

	INFOMERCIAL CLASS EXAMPLE	GROUP INFOMERCIAL
Attention		
Need		

	INFOMERCIAL CLASS EXAMPLE	GROUP INFOMERCIAL
Satisfaction		
Visualization		
Action		

Created by: Renee Kaufmann, University of Kentucky

SHOW AND TELL IMPROMPTU

Goal: To see how students use an item as a visual aid to describe something about themselves.

Rationale: This speech will provide the opportunity for students to show their understanding for incorporating visual aids.

Directions: Do you remember what one of the best parts of school was when you were a kid? *Recess? Maybe. Art projects? Perhaps. Show and Tell? – **ABSOLUTELY***!

As we study visual aids, we are headed back to our childhoods for some good ol' fashioned "Show and Tell." Bring an item with you from home to class next time. It does not have to be from your childhood, although, that is perfectly fine if it is.

The main purpose of this exercise will be to see how you use your item as a visual aid to describe something about yourself.

Do not forget the principles of good organization and delivery as you decide what object to bring and then design a short (1-2 minute) speech.

Created by: Jami Warren, University of Kentucky

GROUP DYNAMICS SUMMATIVE ASSESSMENT FORM

Goal: To create accountability and ownership for each member's actions within the group outside of class.

Rationale: Having students reflect on their contributions as well as others' contributions during the group work process will encourage communication and help foster cohesiveness.

Directions: In a 1-2 page typed, formal paper, reflect on the group process for the actuation symposium speech. This paper should follow the rules of proper grammar, spelling and punctuation and represent your best work. Additionally, this paper is to be completed and included in your portfolio on the day your group presents.

This paper should include the following:

1. A clear overall score out of seven points for each group member. Rate each of your group members' (including your own) overall contributions to the group process using the following rating scale:

1   2   3   4   5   6   7
(Poor)   (Met requirements)   (Excellent)

2. An ethical critique for each group member (including yourself) justifying the score you have assigned.

3. A discussion exploring the advantages and disadvantages of working in your particular group.

4. A reflection on what you have learned about effective strategies for working in groups based on your CIS 111 group work experiences.

Adapted from "Com 181: Public Speaking Workbook" Deanna Sellnow

EXAMPLE GROUP DYNAMICS SUMMATIVE REFLECTION

POSTPARTUM DEPRESSION GROUP

The group made up of Cassie, Lacie, Jessica, and Kyle gave their speeches on depression and I have been assigned to critique them. They all spoke on Wednesday April 6th and this is what I thought of their speeches, as it applies to Ethos, Pathos, and Logos.

I find myself fortunate to have had as great of a group as I did. It is going to be hard for me to rate each person because seeing them actually give the speech would show me more about how committed they were. But, I will try to do my best.

Cassie deserves a seven as far as I am concerned. Throughout the whole process she was a team player. I never saw her deter away from the group goal. Cassie showed dedication and support. She was even willing to cancel a doctor's appointment just to make it to a group meeting. Cassie did miss class one day, but it was for a legitimate reason and she followed the group contract procedures for if a class time was missed. She e-mailed everyone before class and then called us after class to see what she had missed. Post partum depression was Cassie's subject originally and she did a great job of helping the rest of the group get up to speed on what it is about. She displayed her abilities to do well on her own and as part of a group.

Lacie also deserves a seven. Lacie played a different role in the group than Cassie did. She made sure that people were always included and were on the same page during discussions. She met her daily assignments and was instrumental in working with the PowerPoint presentation. Another thing Lacie did well was brainstorming. The majority of the ideas that we have to distinguish ourselves from the other groups come from her. She brought fresh new ideas to the table. Besides doing all that, she was also at every meeting, on time, and prepared. Her upbeat attitude and excitement made working on the speech much more enjoyable, especially considering the topic we have.

Kyle's rating is a little bit harder for me to give. Some days I wanted to give him sevens and other days he deserved threes. Overall, I think I am going to have to give him a five. Kyle was very inconsistent. He missed or was late for a couple of our group meetings outside of class. He didn't help out much with the slide show and wasn't very vocal about any ideas or suggestions he had. On the plus side, I was very impressed that he had his speech done as quickly as he did. He also told us that he likes working in the group because he has to be responsible and get his work done so that he doesn't let everyone down. So, I know that when it comes to the speech, I should be able to count on him to do a good job.

Finally, I get to experience the joy of rating myself. (Can you sense the sarcasm?) If I have to rate myself, I would hand out a six. The main reason I wouldn't give myself a seven is because my outline isn't exactly done yet. I know what my main points are and so the group is able to go from those. However, I am still trying to put the finishing touches on it. This may prohibit me from being able to practice as much as I should before we rehearse as a group. I know I will be ready by Friday though. I haven't been a total slacker the whole time though. I have attended all the meetings. I gave input when it was needed and helped the group brainstorm ideas for the various parts of the project. When it came to finishing the PowerPoint, I made several contributions. Now that I look back, I realize that I could have done more, especially when it came to helping everyone else do research and find supporting material.

Working in this particular group has been a good experience overall. It was refreshing for me to be in a group with other people that were willing to work and do what needed to be done without being asked. While we were thinking of ideas for main points, I found it extremely helpful to have other peoples' opinions on what topics would work and what other ones could be changed. One thing I didn't like about my group was that we didn't really take the time to make sure everyone was on the same page about the main points. It would have been nice if when we were writing our speeches, if we had done it together. That way we could have made our speeches more united. I have learned a great deal from the speech. Not only have I become more knowledgeable about postpartum depression, but I have also learned more about working in groups. I now know that it is very helpful to establish group goals and rules right away. This helped us stay focused and made sure that everyone knew what was expected. Establishing deadlines was good because we were able to get more accomplished. Like I stated earlier, I thought that, overall, my group experience was a positive one.

Taken from "Com 181: Public Speaking Workbook" Deanna Sellnow

COMMUNICATING VISUALLY & DIGITALLY

Visual and Digital Communication

Distributing Messages

KEENELAND CAMPAIGN ANALYSIS

Goal: To examine the key design elements used within each message.

Rationale: Having students examine a popular campaign's visual messages will foster a conversation about what is and is not effective use of visual elements.

Directions: Below are three different ways to reach an audience with one's message (Print, Commercial, Internet). *Note: The examples below are from the same year but different meets.* Look at how the elements within the print ad and commercial are carried out. Next to the print and commercial example explain who is the audience and what is the message being conveyed. Next go to the website and explore how Keeneland uses the Internet to reach their audience.

The following images and links are from Keeneland and/or Cornett IMS websites.

Keeneland's Print Advertising:

Photo courtesy of Keeneland

Keeneland's TV Commercial http://www.youtube.com/watch?v=Za8T9yieJtQ:

Photo courtesy of Keeneland

Created by: Renee Kaufmann, University of Kentucky

Keeneland's Website: http://www.keeneland.com/default.aspx

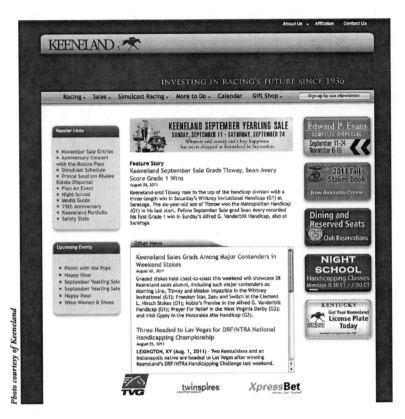

Photo courtesy of Keeneland

QUESTIONS FOR DISCUSSION:

1. How does Keeneland incorporate visual elements within their digital pieces?

2. How are the three advertisements similar? How are they different?

Created by: Renee Kaufmann, University of Kentucky

QUESTIONS FOR DISCUSSION: AUDIENCE ANALYSIS

Goal: Students will analyze a commercial examining what the creator incorporates to persuade and identifying how the message is created for the specific audience member.

Rationale: Having students analyze a commercial's target audience will show the importance of an audience analysis when creating a persuasive message.

Direction: Watch the following commercials and answer the questions below.

1. Who is the audience that this commercial targets (what are the demographic and psychological characteristics associated with this audience?). Why do you think so?

2. During which shows might this commercial air (show, time of day, channel, etc.)? Why would this happen?

3. What is the message presented in each commercial?

   A.

   B.

   C.

4. What might be different about each commercial's message if the same product was targeted towards one of the other audiences?

Created by: Jami Warren, University of Kentucky

QUESTIONS TO GUIDE GROUP WORK DAY (PREWRITING/BRAINSTORMING)

Goal: To keep students on task with their digital assignment.

Rationale: Providing questions will help students conceptualize their projects and stay on task.

Directions: Answer the questions below with your group.

1.

    A. Who do you want to reach with your digital project? In other words, who do you want to persuade to take action?

    B. What are the demographic characteristics associated with this audience?

    C. What are the psychological characteristics associated with this audience (what are their psychological needs)?

2. What types of publications, news/media outlets do this group read/watch to get information?

3. What message do you want to send to your audience about your project? What do you want to persuade them to do?

4. What might be the best way to reach your audience with your message (what types of media might be most appropriate—website, Facebook, newspaper, etc.)?

Created by: Jami Warren and Sarah Kercsmar, University of Kentucky

SAMPLE ESSAYS AND SPEECH OUTLINES

Position Paper

Annotated Bibliography

Rhetorical Analysis (Neo-Aristotelian)

Symposium Outline (Group and Individual)

Position Paper 1: Health Care

The Health Care Problem and Its Solution

Student 1

University of Kentucky

The Health Care Problem and Its Solution

Imagine a person named John who is in his late sixties. He has worked his whole life earning an average salary. He has a wife and two children who have children of their own. He is about to retire with a good amount of savings from his life's work. However, John later finds out from a recent doctor's visit that he has a medical condition that requires extensive treatment. This is a surprise to him as he has been in relatively good health throughout his life. Soon after, John learns of the cost of his treatment is in the thousands. He has no health insurance because of its high cost, and now no insurance company will cover him due to his newly discovered condition. As a result, John loses much of his savings and must re-join the workforce struggling to pay the cost of his healthcare.

This story is fictional, but it is all too familiar with most of the nearly fifty million Americans who are without health insurance (www.aflcio.org/issues/healthcare). Health care is arguably one of the top issues that are being discussed today. It has been an important topic in the past Presidential election, and it continues to be debated on how the problems associated with health care can be solved. Americans, nowadays, receive their insurance from employers, private insurance companies, or the government. However, due to the rising cost of insurance, it is becoming increasingly difficult for Americans to obtain adequate health insurance. A system that provides universal health care financially supported by the government can solve these issues.

The first reason for providing universal health care is of moral basis. It is a right of the people to be provided health care. Everyone should have a right to live or live comfortably in terms of health. In the Constitution, it states that the government should "promote the general welfare". This means that the government should provide security, public education, social programs, and other public services that helps the general citizen. Doesn't health fall into the general welfare category? Shouldn't the government be obligated to keep its citizens in good health? Universal health care is a program that should be provided based on the support of our Constitution written by our Founding Fathers, and they intended for our government to follow these guidelines to better serve our country.

The cost of insurance is the main reason that many Americans lack proper health care. Americans mainly receive health care from their employers such as GE Healthcare, a branch of the company General Electric. However, the feasibility of employers providing health benefits is becoming increasingly difficult. Employers are either dropping health coverage or providing insufficient coverage towards their employees. Health care is simply not affordable. From 2001 to 2005, the average amount that Americans paid for insurance increased by thirty percent, but income only rose three percent (www.health-

careproblems.org). Every year, a total of forty-five thousand Americans die because of not having health insurance (cnnhealth.com). Having a universal health care system is a solution to this problem. No citizen will be rejected health care regardless of pre-existing conditions or money. Bottom line is that more Americans will live.

The efficiency of having an universal health care system can benefit all involved in the medical world. Having a government that regulates everything into one database saves time, work, and money. Imagine if all family physicians, therapists, and surgeons were able to be on the same page because of an universal system. Less paper is used. No more hassle going through procedures required by different health insurance companies. Prescription drugs are bought in bulk instead of individually. Everything is simple which makes things relatively inexpensive. Even the people who care for patients will benefit.

A large argument against universal health care is how this system will be financed. It is a government program so it will be financed by taxes. Raising taxes is an idea that Americans are not supportive of. However, this idea is an exception that Americans should consider. Providing universal health care is not a burden that one citizen takes on. It will be shared among the whole country. We already pay taxes for public services such as highways and education. But, is health care not allowed to considered to be among those services. I argue that it should be one of the top priorities if not the number one priority to provide free health care to anyone that needs it. We are giving up a part of our income to better our country. This is an issue where we need not be selfish and care for our friend or neighbor who struggles to pay his or her medical bills.

Another argument is the uncertainty that an universal system of health care will work. How is it possible to provide free health care to everyone? What about the costs? Is this going to make things worse? These questions can be answered by looking at the health care systems of other countries such as Canada, France, England, and the list goes on. The U.S. is the only industrialized country that does not provide some form of

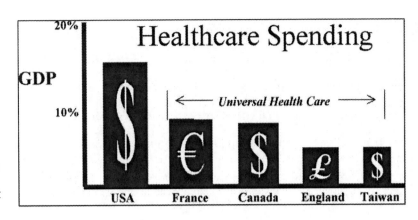

universal health care. This is ironic because the U.S. is one of the richest countries in the world. These other countries serve as models of how it can be done successfully. Citizens of these countries generally live longer and pay less for health care as shown by the chart above. Having a successful system in the U.S. is definitely possible.

Health care has been a lingering issue in recent years. It was at the core of Barack Obama's campaign for Presidency, and it continues to merit discussion in today's debates. It is an issue that hits many Americans. But, it all can be solved with a government funded universal system of health care. It may require tax raises, but it allows everyone to experience a healthy life that is supported by our rights as humans and as a right in our Constitution. Creating a system of health care for all is in my book, a task that has gone undone far too long.

References

BalancedPolitics.org - Universal Health Care (Pros & Cons, Arguments For and Against, Advantages & Disadvantages). (n.d.).*BalancedPolitics.org - Free Balanced, Non-Partisan Discussion of Political & Social Issues for Debate (Pros and Cons - Decision Making Politics).* Retrieved February 2, 2012, from http://www.balancedpolitics.org/univeral_health_care.htm

Health Care Statistics | Health Care Problems. (2012, February 2). *Health Care Problems.*Retrieved February 2, 2012, from http://www.healthcareproblems.org/health-care-statistics.htm

CNN, M. P. (2009, September 18). 45,000 American deaths associated with lack of insurance - CNN.com *.CNN.com - Breaking News, U.S., World, Weather, Entertainment & Video News.* Retrieved February 2, 2012, from http://www.cnn.com/2009/HEALTH/09/

Ireland, J. (2011, August 11). Pros & Cons Of Free Universal Health Care | LIVESTRONG .COM. *LIVESTRONG.COM - Lose Weight & Get Fit with Diet, Nutrition & Fitness Tools | LIVESTRONG.COM.* Retrieved February 2, 2012, from http://www.livestrong.com/article/30692-pros-cons-universal-health/

Swartz, K. (n.d.). BusinessWeek Debate Room Universal Health Care: No Sick Joke. *Businessweek - Business News, Stock Market & Financial Advice.* Retrieved February 2, 2012, from http://www.businessweek.com/debater

Universal Health Care Saves Money By… — Medical Malprocess. (2008, May 1). *Medical Malprocess.* Retrieved February 2, 2012, from http://thesystemmd.com/?p=52

What's Wrong with America's Health Care. (n.d.). *aflcio.org - America's Union Movement.* Retrieved February 2, 2012, from http://www.aflcio.org/issues/healthcare/w

Position Paper 2 and Annotated Bibliography:
Minimum Wage

The Paradox of the Minimum Wage Law

Mustafa Al Sakha

University of Kentucky

The Paradox of the Minimum Wage Law

Recently, the presidential candidate Mitt Romney announced his economic policy about the minimum wage law. Concerned with helping the working poor, he argues in favor of the minimum wage policy and supports the indexation of the minimum wage rate to inflation. The minimum wage law has been a controversial economic issue since it was enacted in 1938, and even in the years before that. Many economists and policy analysts have doubted its advantages in helping the working poor and reducing the poverty even before it was applied. And now, most economists come up with evidence about its drawbacks and adverse effects. However, many politicians and policy makers as well as the working poor still support this policy. I claim that the minimum wage law does not help the working poor because its drawbacks outweigh its benefits, which means it does not do its intended purpose of helping the working poor. The minimum wage policy hurts poor workers in many ways, two of which are: increasing the unemployment rate among the working poor, and benefiting non-poor workers at the expense of poor workers.

First, the minimum wage law does not help the working poor in general because it reduces the number of low-paying job opportunities and the number of work hours available for low-skill workers, and most of those workers already live in or close to poverty. According to the Bureau of Labor Statistics (2009), the number of the working poor in 2009 was 10.4 million workers. So, the unemployment rate among the working poor will be raised by cutting the number of low-skill jobs that is caused by applying or raising the minimum wage law. As a result, the number of the poor will increase dramatically as it will be hard for them to find full-time jobs. Moreover, many poor workers will be laid off because small businesses typically can't afford to pay high payrolls, especially for less-skillful workers. In a study about the effects of the minim wage law on teen unemployment, Sen, Rybczynski , and Waal (2011) argue that "a higher minimum wage may paradoxically result in more poverty as teen unemployment results in a drop in household income among low income families" (p. 29). Another similar study shows that for a 10% increase in the minimum wage rate, there is an overall 1% decrease in the employment of retail sector, and this percentage reaches 3.8% among teenagers in the same sector (Sabia, 2008). These studies and many others show that the minimum wage law has an adverse effect on the employment rate among families who live in poverty. Moreover, many of those workers already earn wage rates that are higher than the federal minimum wage rate (Burkhauser & Sabia, 2007).

This means that the working poor are vulnerable to either reduction in their wages or losing their jobs. Or in the best scenario, their wages stay the same, which does not improve their well-beings. To see how the minimum wage law hurts the working poor consider the following question: what would happen to poor workers who already earn more than the federal minimum wage when they get laid off because of raising the minimum wage, which is intended to improve their well-being? The answer to this question is poverty and unemployment will increase among the working poor.

Another adverse effect of the minimum wage law is that it benefits non-poor workers more than the working poor. When the minimum wage level rise, low-skill jobs become more attractive not only to the working poor but also to non-poor workers, especially teenagers, students, and immigrants. Therefore, the working poor will face a tough competition from the non-poor workers, who are generally more skilled than their poorer counterparts. So, it makes sense that, with higher minimum wage rates, employers would rather employ the more skilled workers than the less-skilled poor workers. One obvious reason for this is that, economically speaking, skilled workers provide more value per dollar and more productivity to employers than less-skill workers. One study shows that the employment rate increases among teenagers who come from wealthier and more educated families because they find the new minimum wage more desirable and worthwhile. In contrast, their poorer counterparts who come from less educated families, especially those who come from single parent households, face higher unemployment due to the net decrease in labor demand and increase in competition (Ahn, Arcidiacono & Wessels, 2011). According to this study, non-poor workers benefit from the higher minimum wage rate because they are willing to accept the higher rate and are more skilled than poor workers. Another study estimated that poor families will receive 12.7% from the benefits of raising the minimum wage to $7.25 an hour. On the other hand, families who earn more than twice the poverty income will receive 63% of the benefits (Burkhauser & Sabia, 2005). These studies show how paradoxically the benefit of the minimum wage law to the non-poor outweighs the benefit to the poor, who are supposed to be the number one beneficiaries of this law.

Even though many policy makers and poor workers as well as some economists advocate raising the minimum wage rate to help the working poor get out of poverty, it turns out that the minimum wage policy hurts the working poor and does not reduce poverty. Raising the minimum wage rate results in the reduction in the number of low-skill jobs available to poor workers and an increase in the competition from non-poor workers for those few jobs. This leads to the following conclusion: the policy has an adverse effect on poverty and, therefore, should be discontinued.

References

Ahn, T., Arcidiacono, P., & Wessels, W. (2011). The distributional impacts of minimum wage increases when booth labor supply and demand are endogenous. *Journal of Business and Economic Statistics, 29*(1), 12-23. doi:10.1198/jbes.2010.07076.

Burkhauser, R. V., & Sabia, J. J. (2007). The effectiveness of minimum-wage increases in reducing poverty: Past, present, and future. *Contemporary Economic Policy, 25*(2), 262-281. doi.10.1111/j.1465-7287.2006.00045.x.

Burkhauser, R. V., & Sabia, J. J. (2005). Raising the minimum wage: Another empty promise to the working poor. *Employment Policies Institute*. Retrieved February 10, 2012, from http://epionline.org/study_detail.cfm?sid=87.

Sabia, J. J. (2008). The effects of minimum wage increases on retail employment and hours: New evidence from monthly CPS data. *Journal Of Labor Research, 30*(1), 75-97.

Sen, A., Rybczynski, K., & Waal, C. V. D. (2011). Teen employment, poverty, and the minimum wage: Evidence from Canada. *Labour Economics,18*(1), 36-47.

U.S. Department of Labor, Bureau of Labor Statistics. (2011). *A Profile of the Working Poor, 2009*. Washington D.C: U.S. Government Printing Office. Retrieved February 11, 2012, from http://www.bls.gov/cps/cpswp2009.pdf.

Annotated Bibliography

Ahn, T., Arcidiacono, P., & Wessels, W. (2011). The distributional impacts of minimum wage increases when booth labor supply and demand are endogenous. *Journal of Business and Economic Statistics, 29*(1), 12-23. doi:10.1198/jbes.2010.07076.

This scholarly journal article found that non-poor benefit from the minimum wage law more than the poor. It is very recent and done by three professors of economics. It supports the arguments of the adverse effect of the policy.

Burkhauser, R. V., & Sabia, J. J. (2007). The effectiveness of minimum-wage increases in reducing poverty: Past, present, and future. *Contemporary Economic Policy, 25*(2), 262-281. doi.10.1111/j.1465-7287.2006.00045.x.

This article argue that the poor already earn more than the minimum wage, most minimum wage beneficiaries live in non-poor households, and the minimum wage policy is a poor tool for anti-poverty. The author of this scholarly article is a senior professor of policy analysis and an academic journal editor. This can be used to show the drawbacks of the minimum wage policy.

Burkhauser, R. V., & Sabia, J. J. (2005). Raising the minimum wage: Another empty promise to the working poor. *Employment Policies Institute*. Retrieved February 10, 2012, from http://epionline.org/study_detail.cfm?sid=87

This study is sponsored by a non-profit organization interested in minimum wage polices and labor situations. It provides analysis of the historical issues surrounding the minimum wage policy. It is helpful in providing a new perspective and evidence about some historical issues and researches.

Sabia, J. J. (2008). The effects of minimum wage increases on retail employment and hours: New evidence from monthly CPS data. *Journal Of Labor Research, 30*(1), 75-97.

The focus of this piece of research is on the effects of the minimum wage on retail sectors. This scholarly article is done by a senior professor who published a lot of studies concerning this policy. This article can be used as across-sector evidence.

Sen, A., Rybczynski, K., & Waal, C. V. D. (2011). Teen employment, poverty, and the minimum wage: Evidence from Canada. *Labour Economics,18*(1), 36-47.

This study shows that increasing the minimum wage in Canada reduces teen employment and lower poor-family income. This can be used to show the effects of the policy across countries.

U.S. Department of Labor, Bureau of Labor Statistics. (2011). *A Profile of the Working Poor, 2009.*

Washington D.C: U.S. Government Printing Office. Retrieved February 11, 2012, from http://www.

bls.gov/cps/cpswp2009.pdf

This government document provides statistics about the labor situation, especially the working poor, in the United States. Statistics on this document can be used as statistical evidence to show the magnitude of the effects of the minimum wage.

Rhetorical Analysis: Coal Mining

Argument Through Imagery

Brittany Turiczek

University of Kentucky

Abstract

This analysis is going to focus on three different images and their applications to the timely issue of coal mining. The three images represent varying aspects of the issue from the point of view of the illustrator or photographer. All three images share the common message that coal mining is detrimental. The first image utilizes the rhetorical strategies pathos and ethos, and is created for the purpose of informing the audience that coal production is negatively affecting the planet. The second image also utilizes the rhetorical strategies pathos and ethos, and is created to show the audience that knowledge concerning where our power comes from is warped. The third image utilizes the rhetorical strategies logos, pathos, and ethos, to deliver the message that although mining is causing destruction, people can still stand up against it. The shared message from all three images is that coal mining affects the environment and our health negatively. This analysis will incorporate the five canons of rhetoric to explore how the three selected images powerfully represent this argument. The images convey this message through the use of rhetorical strategies, style, delivery, and memorable qualities. All of these approaches incorporate together to present the intended message effectively.

Argument Through Imagery

Coal mining has been a common practice in America for centuries. It has only recently become a controversial issue in the past several decades. The reason that it has become such a heated subject recently is for several reasons. The first reason is because America has become more scientifically advanced; therefore allowing us to better understand the effects coal mining has on the environment. Through these advancements it has been proven that coal mining contributes to water pollution, air pollution, soil erosion, and the disturbance of ecosystems. In an analysis completed in 2005, it was found that the total annual cost of external damages from sulfur dioxide, nitrogen oxides, and particulate matter from burning coal for power were about sixty two billion dollars (Romm, 2011). The next reason that coal mining has become controversial is because of the danger associated with it. Coal mining is a highly dangerous practice that involves coal miners having to travel into sealed off mines deep in the earth. This puts the miner at risk if the mine collapses or if there is a fire or gas leak; many miners would not be able to escape the mine. Not to mention long-term exposure to substances in coal mines causes miners to develop cancers and black lung.

The third reason why coal mining has become disputed is because it has become widely spread. The 19th century was when large scale coal mining developed due to the Industrial Revolution. The coal that was mined in the beginning of this time was mainly used for transportation and cooking needs. The coal that is mined now is used for electricity. Electrical power plants burn coal to produce electricity for America. In the 19th century coal was not cultivated as grossly as it is now because it was not needed then for electricity. America's need for electricity is the reason for the massive increase in coal production and can also be seen in the statistic provided by the Center for History, "On a daily basis an average American consumes 20 pounds of coal according to the Washington Post," (Gross & O'Kane, 2010). These are all reasons explaining why coal production has been intensely scrutinized the last few decades. These reasonings are the basis for the analysis for the following three images.

Image courtesy of cartoonist Nick Anderson and the Houston Chronicle

Look at the above image by cartoonist Nick Anderson. What do you feel when you look at this image? Do you feel as if an injustice is being done? Does this image persuade you to want to do something about it? If you responded yes to any of these questions, then you were affected by rhetorical strategy. The rhetorical strategy of ethos and pathos is heavily incorporated into this image. Ethos is an argument based around the character of the person delivering it. In this case the presenter is Nick Anderson, an American cartoonist. Usually cartoonists are little known, and carry little ethical appeal. However, Nick Anderson is widely known. Anderson is a Pulitzer Prize winning cartoonist that has had his cartoons appear in over one hundred newspapers. He also has appeared on television several times, and was a part of the Republican YouTube Presidential debate in 2007. All of this exposure adds to Anderson's influence. Undoubtedly if the audience is aware of Anderson and his notoriety, they will be more willing to trust and accept the message he conveys in the cartoon.

Pathos is an argument based on emotion. Clearly, Anderson uses emotional imagery to represent the argument that the consumption of coal is harmful. The first way that he does this is through the imagery representing that coal consumption is poisoning the environment. When first glancing at the entire image, it's noticed that the left hand side is almost polar opposite to the right. The left hand side seems to resemble hell with barren land, a red sky, and endless greed. This is a portrayal of the direct effects coal burning has on our environment. There are no signs of life in the image other than the fat man. No trees, grass, or animals are present. Also, there is a blood-like haze hanging over the landscape, filled with black soot coming from the power plant. The red sky is symbolic of the war and danger our present environment is being faced with; the red tint also represents the immense power that these distributors and producers of coal energy have. The black pouring soot represents death and evil which obviously corresponds to the mass gravestones and sadness in the image on the right.

Then there are the coal carts, seemingly never ending stretching from the power plant to infinity. This represents the constant burning of coal, the constant destruction of earth. The man although not a traditional representation, is meant to be seen as a figurative devil. He stands in the middle of hell on earth, gleaming with joy and pride exclaiming, "Cheap Energy!" Only the devil would react this way to exposing earth to the poisons shown in the image on the far left, thus killing mass amounts of people shown on the right. Literally, the man represents big business as coal production has become. The largest coal production company in America, Peabody Energy Corporation, is worth about eleven point four billion dollars and mines twenty percent of the coal in the United States (Lundell, 2007). Anderson wants you to question if big companies such as Peabody is concerned with what is happening to the environment or how many people their mines kill. The conclusion Anderson wants the audience to come to is no; the only concern this man, meaning the coal companies, have is how much profit they will make.

The image on the right conveys an entirely different message. It takes place in 'Coal Country'. This represents the areas in America where a large percent of the population works in coal mines because that's the only work that is available. A widow and small child are seen mourning at a grave, assumingly of a miner who died from some sort of mining related incident. Whether this was from a mining accident, or an illness due to coal mining, we cannot be sure. We do know, however, that this is not an isolated incident in the community based on the extensive number of graves. Observing the environment in the graveyard it can be seen that it is opposite of the image on the far left. There are bright green trees and grass. The earth is prospering in this environment because it is not exposed to the toxins of coal production. However, death is present in this image. The woman and small child draped in black represent mourning and death. The woman is seen uttering her response to the man saying, "Not for us...". The widow is expressing her feeling that although the cost of coal might be cheap for business, it stole the life of her loved one, a priceless loss. People, most likely men, are seen now as head-stones, the direct result of being miners. They were brought back to this beautiful setting to be put to rest. The blue and white of the sky represent heaven, faith, and purity. Anderson is conveying the story that the miners have to endure work in hell (the coal mines). Then eventually from working in the mines their lives are possessed by the devil (big business). The men are then laid to rest in the purity of their lush homeland where their family and god are near.

This image is very effective in communicating the illustrator's argument that coal production is harmful. The message is supported through the rhetorical strategy pathos and ethos. The message is not only implied, but strongly represented through imagery. The style and delivery of the message is done non-verbally through imagery, but also it is done honestly. The cartoonist Anderson does not represent false statistics or attempt to persuade through fallacies. Instead, he paints a realistic portrait of what, in his eyes, our country is facing today. This image invokes fear and a call-to-action.

Image courtesy Signe Wilkinson and the Philadelphia Daily News

The next image courtesy of cartoonist Signe Wilkinson intends to represent the idea that our thought towards our energy sources are warped. Analysis of this image will be utilized through the five canons of rhetoric. The first canon of rhetoric concerns how an argument is presented within an image. This image also heavily relies on the rhetorical strategy pathos and ethos. Although, Wilkinson is less known than Anderson as an editorial cartoonist, she still holds influence. Wilkinson also won a Pulitzer Prize for her cartoons; and was actually the first female cartoonist to do so. Wilkinson has a strong following, and could easily have affected viewers of the image who were aware of her influence.

Pathos is also utilized in this image. Pathos is used to present the argument that: while we all are steered to believe America is being protected, in reality we are all contributing to its destruction. The second canon of rhetoric concerns how the image is arranged. The illustrator purposely added in certain details and arranged the cartoon in a way to present a point. In the image the two characters are symbolizing the majority of American, middle-class families. This is shown by the dressy-casual attire of the man and woman, the wine glass on the floor, and also the iPad. You assume that the two are a couple by the way the woman leans over the chair to the man, and the casual way he speaks to her. Also, it is assured that these people are not rich by the worn-out dull looking chair in which the man is sitting in. If the man had been sitting in a luxurious leather couch and the woman draped with diamonds, it would have changed the style of the argument, therefore ruining the ability of the audience to relate. The man is seen commenting about his iPad that, "With no paper, it's, like, totally green!"

Image courtesy of Greenpeace.org

This would normally be seen as a positive comment, as many people with Ipads and other resembling technologies have also stated this 'improvement'. However, while this man and woman are relishing in the fact that they are being crusaders, it shows their power source is plugged into the wall with a soot-covered miner on top. This miner represents the irony of the man's statement. He believes that he is, "…like totally green," when in fact according to the image, he is the complete opposite. This image is very memorable because it is highly relatable to all of us as Americans. Everything in our culture is fueled by technology, which means the majority of us own a tablet or laptop. This has caused an addiction of sorts to our technologies, which in turn means we are somehow always plugged into the wall. This is exactly what Wilkinson wants us to think about when the audience views the image. The intended message is that we, as Americans, are consuming large amounts of electricity all the time and don't even realize what the cost is of that convenient power.

Last of all three images is a photograph from Greenpeace.org. This image intertwines the rhetorical strategies of ethos, logos, and pathos to create a strong message. This image utilizes the rhetorical strategy logos because the photograph's argument is logical in the sense that it is presented in a true manner. This is not a cartoon interpretation of the issue as in the previous images; but instead the picture is a true depiction of coal mining. This photograph provides tangible evidence towards the destruction coal mining causes. This in turn strengthens the over-all message the organization is trying to relay towards the viewer that coal mining should be stopped.

This image also contains the rhetorical strategy ethos because the image is presented by Greenpeace. Greenpeace is a non-government environmental organization that has maintained legitimacy since it was established forty one years ago. Greenpeace is not a political or private organization. Instead, it is a worldwide organization that according to its website Greenpeace.org it, "aims to protect the earth and all of its organisms". The organization has enough reliability and reputation to garner more attention and possibly action due to this image.

Lastly, the image also contains the rhetorical strategy pathos. The photographer arranged the image in a way so that the viewer saw this lone man and his message front and center, while the destruction of the land due to mining was set as the background. This is perfect in catching the viewer's attention by presenting an issue, and representing the issue all at the same time. Any audience who views this image would have to acknowledge that coal mining does damage the environment. Looking at the image of this man who is holding up a sign that says, "Coal-powering climate change," the viewer feels a sense of connection to him. His message is understood that while coal's main purpose is powering electricity, it is also possibly powering climate change. The majority of audience members viewing this image would want to support this man standing alone and support his cause. They might even feel inclined to join the man in the picture. At further analysis of the image, it's observed that the background image exhibits a feeling of hopelessness. It makes the audience feel small, opposed to the large destructive machinery set in the background. The question is then raised how are individuals as this man, supposed stand up to big business, and win? This goal seems impossible. However, when the ethos of the image is remembered and the fact that the large organization Greenpeace is behind causes like these, the viewer then feels as if a solution is possible. This is why the image is memorable because it makes us realize that although the real issue of coal mining is still present, there are even more powerful solutions.

While these three images present the idea that coal production is negative, there is a strong opposition to this ideology. The opposing side of the coal production argument is that the use of coal results in more good than evil. According to the Kentucky Coal Education Project, coal benefits all Americans for several reasons. The first of these reasons, is because coal provides a stable source of energy that doesn't have to be exported from another country. Also, according to this source coal is a cheap source of energy that doesn't nearly do the amount of damage as reported in the past because of recent strict regulations. Coal production specifically in Kentucky provides many jobs and stimulates the economy. According to the source coal production in Kentucky paid over eight hundred million dollars in direct wages, directly employed over nineteen thousand people, and indirectly provided an additional sixty thousand jobs ("Kentucky Coal Education Project," n.d.).

In the end, we as American consumers should be educated on the process of coal consumption. Whether a negative or positive opinion is formed towards coal mining, that is up to each individual. However, it has become such a massively utilized source of energy for America, that it would be detrimental not to know the possible effects it could be having. As the image by Nick Anderson conveys, coal production is killing our environment, and us. The image created by Signe Wilkinson has a similar message, but her image leans more towards Americans ignorance towards the source of electricity. The last image courtesy of Greenpeace focuses on delivering the message that coal production is truly deteriorating the earth, the place we all call home. Through the rhetorical strategies of pathos, logos, and ethos, all three sources are highly successful in conveying these messages through the images. All three images share the common intent to educate the public about the issue of coal consumption. The desired result of this awareness is for people to start asking themselves questions, such as is our power worth the repercussions? Is electricity worth countless lives? What about the well-being of our planet? This issue and these illustrations throughout the paper contain exigency because this is a very timely issue. As a result of viewing these images, what is your opinion on coal production in America?

References

Gross, R. & O'Kane, T. (2010, Apr. 06). Retrieved Feb. 20, 2012, from http://envhist.wisc.edu

Anderson, N. (2010, Apr. 06). Retrieved Feb. 20, 2012, from http://blog.chron.com

Lundell, D. (2007, Sept. 11). Retrieved Feb. 20, 2012, from http://stocks.investopedia.com

Romm, J. (2011, Feb. 17). Retrieved Feb. 20, 2012, from http://grist.org

Wilkinson, S. (2010, Apr. 07). Retrieved Feb. 20, 2012, from http://thecomicnews.com

Wilson, M. (2009, Aug.). Retrieved Feb. 20, 2012, from http://weblog.greenpeace.org

(n.d.). Retrieved Mar. 04, 2012, from http://www.coaleducation.org/q&a/10_reasons_why_coal.htm

Symposium Outline: Antibacterial Products

ACTUATION PERSUASIVE SYMPOSIUM SPEECH EXAMPLE
MONROE'S MOTIVATED SEQUENCE DESIGN

Formal Outline: "The Dirty Truth about Antibacterial Products"

Jennifer Gilderhus, Megan Gilderhus, Stephanie Ahlfeldt, and Daniel Grothues

INTRODUCTION

I. **Attention Catcher:** A meticulously dressed man in a suit and overcoat squeezed his way through the rush-hour crowd as he boarded the New York City subway. As he braced himself for the ride ahead, he noticed a sign above him that read, "You are the 423rd person to touch that pole today!" Nearby another advertisement warned, "The last guy to touch that pole was named Sal Monella."

II. **Listener Relevance:** Just think of the hundreds of people who have sat in that very seat, touched that same spot in front of you. How many of those people did not wash their hands in the bathroom before sitting there?

III. **Speaker Credibility:** Through our research, we have found that America's obsession with germs is being fueled by misleading advertising and overzealous use of antibacterial products.

IV. **Thesis:** Americans' overuse of antibacterial products is reducing their effectiveness as germ fighters.

V. **Preview:** Today we're going to get down and dirty with germs. Jennifer Gilderhus will be the moderator. Megan Gilderhus will identify the abuse of antibacterial products and will describe its dangerous results, Daniel Grothues will propose a more practical solution for germ removal, and Stephanie Ahlfeldt will visualize a continued future of antibacterial overuse. Together, we will propose a more realistic approach for germ protection; one that includes the practical use of antibacterial products.

Transition: Most of us have heard of these products, many of us buy them and use them regularly. Megan will begin by telling us why these products are not as effective as we would like them to be.

BODY

I. **First Main Point (Need-Problem):** Americans are overusing antibacterial products.

Listener Relevance: You might be familiar with the way a disk jockey overplays a new song on the radio. After a few days, you are tired of hearing the same songs over and over. In that same way, Americans are overusing antibacterial products.

   A. **Subpoint:** We are obsessed with being clean and will buy any product that promises complete germ removal.

      1. **Sub-Subpoint:** The May 9, 1999, edition of the *Washington Post* reports how one lady's obsession with being clean led her to buy an antibacterial pizza cutter and Calvin Klein antibacterial socks!

      2. **Sub-Subpoint:** One in five Americans has a family member who is obsessed with germs. (Rosin, 1997, p. On-line).

      3. **Sub-Subpoint:** 39% of Americans said they have changed their cleaning habits due to germs. (Rosin, 1997, p. On-line).

      4. **Sub-Subpoint:** Last year alone, retailers sold $400 million worth of antibacterial products (Rosin, 1999, p. On-line).

   B. **Subpoint:** Antibacterial product advertising creates a false sense of security.

      1. **Sub-Subpoint:** A recent survey conducted for the Infectious Disease Society of America found that nearly half of all soaps on the market now contain antibacterial agents (Leland, 2000, p. On-line).

      2. **Sub-Subpoint:** According to Dr. S. Levy of Tufts University, "At best these products are ineffective. Even if one did work when first applied, as its level of concentration dropped, bacteria could produce strains that resist it," (Leland, 2000, p. On-line).

      3. **Sub-Subpoint:** In response to this threat, the American Medical Association suggested government regulation for antibacterial products (Leland, 2000, p. On-line).

Transition: Thank you Megan for highlighting some of the problems with antibacterial products. Please continue by bringing to our attention the consequences of our overuse.

II. **Second Main Point (Need-Cause):** An effect of antibacterial product overuse is reduced effectiveness.

Listener Relevance: None of us like to feel dirty – especially Americans. That's why we take showers or baths, wear cologne and perfume and buy hundreds of products that will make us smell better and feel cleaner.

A. **Subpoint:** Overuse of antibacterial products may increase illness and bring on new germs.

1. **Sub-Subpoint:** There is a growing contention that we don't have enough dirt and germs in our lives. (Leland, 2000, p. On-line).

2. **Sub-Subpoint:** According to the September 12, 2000, Minneapolis *Star Tribune*, a few studies show that this crusade for cleanliness may have gone too far. Researchers believe our progress in domestic hygiene may be responsible for the increased rates of asthma, eczema, hay fever, and allergies and may open the venue for new germs.

3. **Sub-Subpoint:** As Dr. Andrew Liu, Pediatric Asthma Specialist at the National Jewish Medical Research Center in Denver states in the aforementioned *Tribune* article, "We're finding that childhood exposure to infections and certain environmental toxins seems to have a protective effect."

B. **Subpoint:** Bacteria are showing signs of resistance to antibacterial agents.

1. **Sub-Subpoint:** New studies are showing that more and more bacteria are becoming impervious to antibacterial agents in "germ killing" soaps and cleansers. (Kolata, 2001, p. On-line).

2. **Sub-Subpoint:** Popular antibacterial hand soaps provide extra protections, but they do not sterilize hands and they are not approved by the FDA. (Davis, 1999, p. On-line).

Transition: As Megan has described, our overuse is a serious problem. Daniel will now propose a more practical solution for germ control.

III. **Third Main Point (Satisfaction-Solution):** Our suggestion for practical germ protection is three-fold. Consumer awareness, moderated use of antibacterial products, and proper hygiene practices are the focus of our solution.

Listener Relevance: I'm sure almost all of us have bought a product because of cool labeling or an attractive advertisement. We can still feel clean and avoid unsightly germs by being more alert to product advertising.

A. **Subpoint:** Antibacterial product advertising promises much more than most products can produce.

1. **Sub-Subpoint:** The first thing to know is that many scientists and government officials have complained that the advertising of these products is misleading, and the Environmental Protection Agency has disciplined several companies for exaggerated claims. (Rosin, 1999, P. On-line).

2. **Sub-Subpoint:** Hasbro advertised that its antibacterial toys and highchairs "protect your child from germs and bacteria." The EPA made Hasbro change the claim after it was found untrue. (Rosin, 1999, p. On-line).

B. **Subpoint:** If you do use antibacterial products, use them in moderation.

   1. **Sub-Subpoint:** We've gone overboard trying to kill everything in the environment. (Kolata, 2001, p. On-line).

   2. **Sub-Subpoint:** As a result, the Federal Trade Commission has begun cracking down on germ-fighting claims being made for a growing number of antibacterial products. (Mayer, 1999, p. On-line).

   3. **Sub-Subpoint:** Jodie Bernstein, Director of the FTC's Bureau of Consumer Protection says, "the message we hope to send consumers is 'Don't think that these products give you any better protection than washing your hands with soap and hot water.' " (Mayer, 1999, p. On-line).

C. **Subpoint:** For practical germ removal, the solution is simple.

   1. **Sub-Subpoint:** Handwashing. This is the tip mentioned first by everyone. It sounds simple, but it is still the best way to prevent infection. (Burcum, 2000, p. On-line).

   2. **Sub-Subpoint:** However, doing it correctly is important. The U.S. Centers for Disease Control and Prevention recommends this process: wet hands with warm soap and water, lather up with soap, rub hands together briskly for 10 seconds, rinse, and dry off with a paper towel. (Burcum, 2000, p. On-line).

Transition: Dr. Marc Micozzi, chairman of the National Hygiene Foundation supports and practices this solution to germ control. Stephanie will now visualize a future without limited use of antibacterial products.

  IV. **Fourth Main Point (Visualization):** Continued abuse of antibacterial products presents a dangerous future for germ control.

Listener Relevance: We've all heard stories on the news about colds and flus developing in new, never before seen strains.

  A. **Subpoint:** Strains of resistant bacteria will develop.

   1. **Sub-Subpoint:** A Tufts University Health & Nutrition Letter from October 1998 states that overkill can backfire. "It can lead to the development of bacteria that will be able to withstand the action of antibacterial agents should they ever really be needed." (Antibacterial Overkill, 1998)

   2. **Sub-Subpoint:** Stuart Levy explains in a *New York Times* article, "Like antibiotics, anti-bacterials can alter the mix of bacteria; they simultaneously kill susceptible bacteria and promote the growth of resistant strains... and now are available to thrive thanks to the destruction of competing microbes." (Brody, 2000)

B. **Subpoint:** Bacteria will mutate and we will run out of defenses.

   1. **Sub-Subpoint:** "The more they're used, the more the bacteria that they are supposed to destroy will undergo mutations that only serve to strengthen them by allowing them to 'resist' the antibacterial attacks." (Antibacterial Overkill, 1998)

   2. **Sub-Subpoint:** As the June 28, 2000, Minneapolis *Star Tribune* describes, "Chemicals can stick around in the home and continue to select for resistance when the levels of these chemicals drop. Then even high levels of the chemicals won't work." (Brody, 2000)

Transition: Stephanie has clearly described the dangerous possibilities of antibacterial product abuse. Luckily, the future for germ control doesn't have to be so bleak.

CONCLUSION

   I. **Action/(Action Step):** YOU can protect yourself from germs without antibacterial products. The solution is simple… Wash Your Hands! Ironically, the American that cleans with antibacterial products shows an astonishing unwillingness to take such a simple step. According to the American Society of Microbiology, a study of 7,836 people in restrooms in Chicago, Atlanta, New York, New Orleans and San Francisco, just 58 percent washed their hands! (Kolata, 2001, p. On-line)

   II. **Listener Relevance:** It doesn't matter where you are or what you are doing. If you are getting on the subway, speaking on a public phone, or sitting in your classroom – you can protect yourself from germs without the use of antibacterial products.

   III. **Speaker Credibility:** Through our research, we've found that America's obsession with germs can be handled effectively without the use of antibacterial products.

   IV. **Thesis Restatement:** We hope we've convinced you that America's overuse of antibacterial products is indeed reducing their effectiveness as germ fighters.

   V. **Main Point Summary:** Today, Megan identified the abuse of antibacterial products and described the dangerous consequences, Stephanie proposed a future of continued abuse, and Daniel detailed a simple solution to an increasingly complex problem.

   VI. **Clincher:** The next time you're boarding the subway or sitting in class – remember, you can be germ free – without the use of antibacterial products.

References

Brody, J. (2000, June 28). 'Antibacterial' may be antihealthy bacteria-killing cleansers and products actually may help create the superbug that many fear, health experts warn. *Star Tribune,* p. 2E.

Brody, J. (2000, June 20). How germ-phobia can lead to illness. *New York Times*, p. 8F.

Burcum, J. (2000, Dec. 19). Debugging the holidays: Spreading cheer doesn't have to mean spreading germs – or getting them. *Star Tribune*, p. 1E.

Davis, E. A. (1999, Oct. 24). Despite questions of efficacy, antibacterials clean up; hygiene: sales of germ-killing consumer products are booming, despite warnings that they could lead to super-bugs resistant to antibiotics. *The Los Angeles Times*, p. 9

Kolata, G. (2001, Jan. 7). Kill all the bacteria! *New York Times,* p. 4.1.

Leland, J. (2000, Aug. 31). Yes, there's such a thing as too clean. *New York Times,* p. F.1.

Leland, J. (2000, Sep. 12). Too clean? Studies show it's possible. *Star Tribune*, p. 1E.

Mayer, C. E. (1999, Sep. 17) FTC challenges antibacterial product claims. *The Washington Post*, p. A9.

Rosin, H. (1999, May 9). Germ warfare. *The Washington Post*, p. W6.

(1998). Antibacterial overkill. *Tufts University Health & Nutrition Letter,* 16, 1-4.

ACTUATION PERSUASIVE SYMPOSIUM SPEECH EXAMPLE
INDIVIDUAL MEMBER OUTLINE EXAMPLE

Formal Outline: "Problems with Antibacterial Products"
Megan Gilderhus

INTRODUCTION

I. **Attention Catcher:** The November 10th, 1997 edition of *The New Republic* states that half of all Americans go out of their way to buy antibacterial products whenever possible.

II. **Listener Relevance:** As consumers, we should all be concerned about antibacterial overuse.

III. **Speaker Credibility:** Through my research, I've learned that antibacterial products lose their effectiveness when not used in moderation.

IV. **Thesis:** Practical, not obsessive, use of antibacterial products is essential for total germ protection.

V. **Preview:** Today, I'll discuss our overuse of antibacterial products. I'll point out the misleading advertising that gives us a false sense of security and finally, I'll warn you of the dangerous consequences of antibacterial product overuse.

Transition: Let's start by looking at the overuse of antibacterial products.

BODY

I. **First Main Point:** Americans are overusing antibacterial products.
Listener Relevance: Have you ever noticed how often disk jockeys replay new songs on the radio? After a while, you get tired of hearing the same songs. Similar to this overplay is America's overuse of antibacterial products.

   A. **Subpoint:** We are obsessed with being clean and will buy any product that promises complete germ removal.

      1. **Sub-Subpoint:** One in five Americans has a family member who is obsessed with germs. (Rosin, 1997, p. On-line).

      2. **Sub-Subpoint:** 39% of Americans said they have changed their cleaning habits due to germs. (Rosin, 1997, p. On-line).

B. **Subpoint:** Antibacterial product advertising creates a false sense of security.

C. **Subpoint:** A recent survey conducted for the Infectious Disease Society of America found that nearly half of all soaps on the market now contain antibacterial agents (Leland, 2000, p. On-line).

Transition: Now that I've discussed some of the problems with antibacterial products, I'll describe the consequences of our overuse.

II. **Second Main Point:** An effect of antibacterial product overuse is reduced effectiveness.
   Listener Relevance: None of us like to feel dirty. We take showers or baths, wear cologne and perfume and apply deodorants and powders daily. Unfortunately, this "need to be clean" can be dangerous.

   A. **Subpoint:** Overuse of antibacterial products may increase illness and bring on new germs.

      1. **Sub-Subpoint:** There is a growing contention that we don't have enough germs and dirt in our lives.

      2. **Sub-Subpoint:** As Dr. Andrew Liu, pediatric asthma specialist at the National Jewish Medical Research Center in Denver, states in the aforementioned *Tribune* article, "We're finding that childhood exposure to infections and certain environmental toxins seems to have a protective effect."

   B. **Subpoint:** Bacteria are showing signs of resistance to antibacterial agents.

   C. **Sub-Subpoint:** Popular antibacterial hand soaps provide protection, but they do not sterilize hands and they are not approved by the FDA. (Davis, 1999, p. On-line).

CONCLUSION

I. **Thesis Restatement:** In conclusion, practical, not obsessive use of antibacterial products is essential for total germ protection.

II. **Main Point Summary:** Today, we have discussed Americans' overuse of antibacterial products and how this may lower effectiveness of antibacterial products.

III. **Clincher:** As stated in the November 10, 1997, edition of *The New Republic*, half of all Americans buy antibacterial products whenever possible, but with this new information, I hope you think twice about making that purchase.

References

Davis, E.A. (1999, Oct. 24). Despite questions of efficacy, antibacterials clean up. *The Los Angeles Times.*

Taken from "Com 181: Public Speaking Workbook" Deanna Sellnow

ACTUATION PERSUASIVE SYMPOSIUM SPEECH EXAMPLE
INDIVIDUAL MEMBER OUTLINE EXAMPLE

Formal Outline: "Visualizing the Future"
Stephanie Ahlfeldt

INTRODUCTION

I. **Attention Catcher:** It's the bleak winter season again… and every other person seems to be ill and determined to spread his or her germs. The grocery store checker sneezes as she scans the produce. The man on the train coughs constantly as his seatmate scrunches against the window and turns her head away… But there also is a counter-insurgency out there, armed with an arsenal of hand soaps, sprays for the bathroom and kitchen countertops, dishwashing detergents, lotions, Band-Aids, toothbrushes, toothpaste, even chopsticks with chemicals guaranteed to kill household germs. The army is deployed despite scientists' repeated warnings that the more you try to kill germs, the stronger they become. Not only are new studies showing that more and more bacteria are becoming impervious to antibiotics, but there are studies showing that, at least in the laboratory, bacteria can become resistant to the germ-killing chemicals in soap and cleansers.

II. **Listener Relevance:** This is a scary story for us to hear being we all use antibacterial products, even if it is just to wash our hands after using a public restroom. This *New York Times* article from January 7, 2001, points out important information for us to consider.

III. **Speaker Credibility:** Personally, I use antibacterial products daily and am surprised to find in my research that I may actually be harming myself and others.

IV. **Thesis:** Continued abuse of antibacterial products presents a dangerous future for germ control.

V. **Preview:** Today, we will examine our future with the continued use of antibacterial products. We will discuss the possibilities of resistant bacteria strains developing, and the mutation of bacteria that we will eventually not be able to defend against.

Transition: Let's start by examining the possibility of resistant bacteria developing.

BODY

I. **First Main Point:** Strains of resistant bacteria will develop.

    A. **Subpoint:** A Tufts University Health & Nutrition Letter from October 1998 states that overkill can backfire. "It can lead to the development of bacteria that will be able to withstand the action of antibacterial agents should they ever really be needed."

    B. **Subpoint:** Stuart Levy explains in a *New York Times* article, "Like antibiotics, antibacterials can alter the mix of bacteria; they simultaneously kill susceptible bacteria and promote the growth of resistant strains... and now are available to thrive thanks to the destruction of competing microbes."

Transition: The thought of resistant strains developing is a very serious problem, but what about when bacteria begin to mutate and we run out of defense?

II. Second Main Point: Bacteria will mutate and we will run out of defenses.

    A. **Sub-Subpoint:** "The more they're used, the more the bacteria that they are supposed to destroy will undergo mutations that only serve to strengthen them by allowing them to 'resist' the antibacterial attacks." (Antibacterial Overkill, 1998)

    B. **Sub-Subpoint:** The *Star Tribune* from June 28, 2001, describes, "Chemicals can stick around in the home and continue to select for resistance when the levels of these chemicals drop. Then even high levels of the chemicals won't work." (Brody, 2000)

Transition: Now it is easy to see how dangerous the overuse of antibacterial products truly is.

CONCLUSION

I. **Thesis Restatement:** Continued abuse of antibacterial products does, in fact, present a dangerous future for germ control.

II. **Main Point Summary:** Today, we have examined our future with the continued use of antibacterial products. We discussed the possibilities of resistant bacteria strains developing and the mutation of bacteria that we will not be able to defend against.

III. **Clincher:** The next time you are in public and are exposed to people coughing and sneezing, avoid reaching for your hand sanitizer. It could make next winter's cold even worse!

References

Brody, J. (2000, June 28). 'Antibacterial' may be antihealthy bacteria-killing cleansers and products actually may help create the superbug that many fear, health experts warn. *Star Tribune,* p. 2E.

Brody, J. (2000, June 20). How germ-phobia can lead to illness. *New York Times*, p. 8F.

Kolata, G. (2001, Jan. 7). Kill all the bacteria! *New York Times,* p. 4.1.

Tufts University (1998). "Antibacterial overkill." Tufts University *Health and Nutrition Letter,* 16, 1-4.

ACTUATION PERSUASIVE SYMPOSIUM SPEECH EXAMPLE
INDIVIDUAL MEMBER OUTLINE EXAMPLE

Formal Outline: "Solutions to Germ Removal"
Daniel Grothues

INTRODUCTION

    I. **Attention Catcher:** How can we help prevent the spread of resistant bacteria?

    II. **Listener Relevance:** We all have to be more responsible.

    III. **Speaker Credibility:** Through my research I have developed a plan of action that everyone can easily follow.

    IV. **Thesis:** There are several alternative solutions to germ removal.

    V. **Preview:** Today, we'll examine some alternative solutions to antibacterial products. In particular, the solution can be found through the use of regular soap and by simply being more practical with antibacterial products.

Transition: According the Minneapolis *Star Tribune*, December 19, 2000, hand washing with regular soap is still the best way to prevent infection.

BODY

    I. **First Main Point:** Antibacterial products advertising promises more than most products can produce, thus the consumer has to develop an awareness of this fact.

        A. **Subpoint:** According to many scientists and government officials advertising on these products is misleading. Also, the Environmental Protection Agency (EPA) has disciplined several companies for exaggerated claims.

        B. **Subpoint:** Hasbro advertised that its antibacterial toys and highchairs "protect your child from germs and bacteria." The EPA made Hasbro change the claim after it was found untrue.

Transition: While increased awareness is a solution for practical germ protection, moderated use of these products is the best alternative.

II. **Second Main Point:** If you do use antibacterial products, use them in moderation.

    A. **Sub-Subpoint:** We've gone overboard trying to kill everything in the environment.

    B. **Sub-Subpoint:** As a result the Federal Trade Commission (FTC) has begun cracking down on germ-fighting claims being made for a growing number of antibacterial products.

    C. **Sub-Subpoint:** Jodie Bernstein, Director of the FTC's Bureau of Consumer Protection says, "the message we hope to send consumers is 'Don't think that these products give you any better protection than washing your hands with soap and hot water.' "

Transition: Not just the moderated use of antibacterial products, but also proper hygiene practices are the focus of our solution.

III. **Third Main Point:** For practical germ removal, the solution is simple.

    A. **Sub-Subpoint:** Hand-washing. This is the tip mentioned first by everyone. It sounds simple, but it is still the best way to prevent infection.

    B. **Sub-Subpoint:** However, doing it correctly is important. The U.S. Center for Disease Control and Prevention recommends this process: Wet hands with warm soap and water, lather up with soap, rub hands together briskly for 10 seconds, rinse, and dry off with a paper towel.

Transition (optional):

CONCLUSION

I. **Thesis Restatement:** In conclusion, there are several alternative solutions to germ removal.

II. **Main Point Summary:** Today, we discussed several solutions to germ removal. Be an alert consumer, moderate your use of antibacterial products, and practice proper hygiene habits.

III. **Clincher:** By now you should have an idea of how to be an aware consumer to prevent the spread of resistant bacteria.

References

Mayer, C.E. (1999, Sep. 17) FTC challenges antibacterial product claims. *The Washington Post*, p. A9.

Burcum, J. (2000, Dec. 19). Debugging the holidays: Spreading cheer doesn't have to mean spreading germs – or getting them. *Star Tribune*, p. 1E.

Taken from "Com 181: Public Speaking Workbook" Deanna Sellnow